Workbook

WITH KEY

Intermediate

Matters

JAN BELL
ROGER GOWER

Longman

Contents chart

Grammar	Vocabulary	Pronunciation
Less direct questions; the definite article; *So do I. / Neither do I.*	Strong adjectives (*exhausted*, etc.); housework; everyday expressions	
Present Simple or Present Continuous?; *How often?*	Clothes; parts of speech; jobs; names and titles	
Time expressions; *used to*; irregular Past Simple forms; pronunciation of Past Simple forms; past tenses and linkers	Countries and nationalities; family relationships; spelling	
Past Simple or Present Perfect?; *been or gone*?; question tags	Living in Britain (shops); American English	
Will or *going to*?; *will* or *shall*?; verbs and preposition	Weather – temperature; telephone expressions; same words, different meanings	Different words, same pronunciation
Defining relative clauses; result and reason; clauses of purposes	Town and country; adjectives with *-ing* or *-ed*	
Adjective word order; possessives	Adjectives and adverbs; relationships; parts of the body	Sound and spelling
Comparison of adjectives and adverbs; superlatives; prepositions of place; prepositions of direction	Furniture and household objects; doing things in the house; forming adjectives; prefixes	
Open conditionals; asking questions; certainty and possibility	Health; synonyms; antonyms	Word stress
Time clauses; *if* or *when*?; future forms; Future Passive	Phrasal verbs with *on* or *off*; phrasal verbs with *take*; describing objects – size and shape	
Functions: requesting and asking permission; apologising and making excuses	Adjectives into nouns; cooking	Short and long vowels; sound and spelling
The second conditional; conditionals and *wish*; prepositional phrases	Buying	Vowel sounds
Since or *for*?; *How long…*?; Present Perfect Simple or Continuous?; Present or Present Perfect?	Idiomatic expressions: pairs	
Necessary or not necessary?; permission and prohibition; obligation, prohibition and permission (past)	Synonyms; groups of words; words often confused	Weak forms
Countable or uncountable?; quantity	Food; eating and drinking; phrasal verbs	
Reporting statements and questions; reporting verbs	Animals; classifications	Problem consonants
The *-ing* form; *-ing* or *to*?	Fear; adjectives and prepositions; adjectives into verbs	
Past Perfect or Past Simple?; Past Perfect Simple or Continuous; sequencing events	Ways of speaking; *say, speak, tell* or *talk*?; *make* or *do*?	Diphthongs
The passive	Words often confused	Contrastive stress; silent letters
Review of verb forms; sentence transformation; spot the errors	Word building; test your vocabulary	Sounds

My favourite things

READING

1   Read the extract below, which is from an article about the actress Jenny Agutter. Then on a separate sheet of paper write down what she does:

	in Los Angeles	in Britain
a) in the morning	_____	_____
b) in the afternoon	_____	_____
c) in the evening	_____	_____

SUNDAY BEST

Actress Jenny Agutter talks about her Sundays on both sides of the Atlantic.

'Whether I'm at home in Los Angeles or staying in England Sunday is a day to relax, and so there are no alarms set.

In California breakfast is fruit and yoghurt followed by pancakes and lots of coffee. Most of the morning is spent reading the newspaper, eating pancakes and pottering around the house doing things like gardening or tidying up. However, I don't iron on a Sunday. My pet hates are ironing and washing up.

In the afternoon I go out on my bike – maybe to the beach, where there are lots of people around, and it's very lively. Otherwise I drive into the hills near Hollywood and walk in the forests. This is really wonderful, because there are some beautiful waterfalls and it's usually very quiet there.

Later in the afternoon I have friends round and we either have a barbecue or go out to a Chinese restaurant. In the evening I stay in and watch a late night movie or a video. I particularly love old Cary Grant films.

When I'm staying in England I stay with my parents, who live in Brixton, or rent a place if I'm filming. Sunday is still a late morning. I may have a croissant and a cup of coffee for breakfast but I don't eat much because I look forward to a traditional English Sunday lunch. I don't mind cooking, so I spend the morning doing that. I love roast lamb so I usually have that, followed by sherry trifle.

Lunch is a time for seeing family and friends, so it usually takes a long time – eating, drinking wine and relaxing.

If I don't cook it's nice to go and have Sunday lunch at a country pub. I really miss pubs, and Guinness, when I'm in LA. I have always loved walking since I was a child, so if I'm in London I enjoy a stroll along the canal in Regent's Park in the afternoon. I always leave the newspapers until the evening when I'm over here, and I buy them all – from the gossipy ones to the serious ones. I probably have just a light meal in the evening and again spend the evening watching television rather than going out.

I'm so busy during the week that Sunday has become my most precious day. It is one of the few days that I get eight hours sleep, which sets me up for the next week.'

(from *Woman's Realm*)

2 Complete the following sentences based on the text.

a) Jenny is tidy in the house but can't stand
_____*ironing*_____ and _____.

b) She adores _____ for walks in the forest.

c) Jenny loves _____ old Cary Grant films.

d) In England she doesn't mind _____ on Sunday morning.

e) She sometimes likes _____ lunch in country pubs.

f) She enjoys _____ along the canal in the afternoon.

3 What questions do you think the interviewer asked Jenny?

a) INTERVIEWER: _____
_____?

JENNY: Yoghurt, pancakes and coffee.

b) INTERVIEWER: _____
_____?

JENNY: In Brixton.

c) INTERVIEWER: _____
_____?

JENNY: No, I usually stay in and watch television.

d) INTERVIEWER: _____
_____?

JENNY: Cary Grant ones.

4 Some of the interviewer's questions required only short answers. Complete the following answers.

a) INTERVIEWER: Do your parents live in California?
JENNY: _____

b) INTERVIEWER: Are you keen on cycling?
JENNY: _____

c) INTERVIEWER: Have you got a house in Britain?
JENNY: _____

d) INTERVIEWER: Can you cook?
JENNY: _____

VOCABULARY

Strong adjectives

5 Use words from the box to complete the gaps below. Mark the stressed syllable, as in the example.

| exhausted   delicious   filthy   enormous |
| furious   tiny |

a) 'You look tired.' 'Yes, I'm _*ex'hausted.*_____

b) 'The house is a bit dirty.' 'Yes, it's
_____. I need to clean it.'

c) 'The food in that restaurant is very good, isn't it?' 'Yes, it's _____.'

d) 'Their kitchen is very big.' 'Yes, it's
_____.'

e) 'What a small dog!' 'I've never seen one so
_____.'

f) 'Are you angry with him?' 'Angry? I'm so
_____ I can hardly speak!'

Housework

6 Write down what the people are doing.

a) Mark _is vacuuming._

b) Sonia _____

c) Steve _____

d) Peter _____

e) Kate _____

Everyday expressions

7 These are some common expressions in everyday English. Match the expressions in column A with the responses in column B.

	A		B
a)	'I'm afraid I'm late.'	1	'Yes, you too.'
b)	'How are you getting on?'	2	'It doesn't matter.'
c)	'What do you do?'	3	'Cheers. See you!'
d)	'Have a nice weekend.'	4	'Yes, help yourself.'
e)	'Goodbye.'	5	'Pleased to meet you.'
f)	'Could I have some more?'	6	'I'm an architect.'
g)	'This is John Adams.'	7	'Very well, thank you.'

GRAMMAR

Less direct questions

8 A tourist wants to catch a train from London to Glasgow. Make her questions less direct.

a) Where is platform 6?

Could you tell me _where platform 6 is_ ?

b) When does the train leave?

Do you know what time _____

_____ ?

c) When does the train arrive?

Would you mind telling me _____

_____ ?

d) Is there a restaurant car on this train?

I'd like to know if _____

_____

e) Where can I buy a ticket?

Can you show me where _____

_____ ?

The definite article

9 Underline the correct alternative below.

a) I am very keen on _chocolate / the chocolate_.

b) It was a red hat with _flowers / the flowers_ on it.

c) Could you get me _a knife / the knife_ to cut this bread with? They're in the drawer.

d) Here is _a book / the book_ I was talking about.

e) 'Do you like _children / the children_?' 'Not really, although I like _children / the children_ who live next door.'

f) I love _foreign food / the foreign food_, especially _Japanese food / the Japanese food_.

So do I / Neither do I

10 Agree with the following statements, using the cues in brackets.

a) I think English is an easy language. (_John_)

So does John.

b) I can't swim very far, unfortunately. (_he_)

_____

c) She's got a new car. (_we_)

_____

d) We haven't got much money. (_I_)

_____

e) Terry's dog barks a lot. (_Malcolm's_)

_____

f) Our house isn't very big. (_ours_)

_____

WRITING

11 Write a paragraph on a separate sheet of paper describing what you do on a typical Sunday. Write about what you eat, how you spend your day and what you like and dislike doing.

How do I look?

VOCABULARY

Clothes

1 Read this fashion advertisement and fill in the labels (1 to 12) in the picture. Use a dictionary if necessary.

1 _____raincoat_____

2 _____

3 _____

4 _____

5 _____

6 _____

7 _____

8 _____

9 _____

10 _____

11 _____

12 _____

QUIETLY CASUAL

Suzanna is wearing a white cardigan and dark shorts from Brown's and sandals from The Natural Shoe Store; a bracelet from Buffer's. Liz is wearing a light raincoat, belt and scarf from Selfridges; a necklace by Mann. Grant is wearing an overcoat; gloves from John Lewis and socks from Sock Shop; his earring is from Liberty.

Parts of speech

2 Write a word from the advertisement in each of the spaces below.

a) noun: _____   c) adjective: _____

b) verb: _____   d) adverb: _____

Jobs

3 What jobs do the following people do? Fill in the gaps and mark the stressed syllable. You might need to use a bilingual dictionary to help you.

a) Nigel arranges funerals. He's an *'undertaker.*

b) Helen looks after people's teeth. She's a

d_____.

c) Ricardo works in a library. He's a

l_____.

d) Noelle plans new buildings. She's an

arc_____.

e) Silvio is in charge of the accounts. He's an

ac_____.

f) Frank repairs water pipes. He's a

pl_____.

g) Angelica fits electrical apparatus. She's an

el_____.

h) Petra designs engines. She's an

en_____.

i) Alan advises people about the law. He's a

l_____.

j) Elisabetta performs medical operations. She's a

sur_____.

Names and titles

Alice Ann Dawson married Tom William Grier but preferred to be called Ms Dawson not Mrs Grier.

4 Answer the following questions. A dictionary may help you.

a) What is Tom's surname?

_____

b) What are Alice's initials?

_____

c) What do we call the names Ann and William?

_____

d) What does the title *Ms* stand for?

_____

e) What does the title *Mrs* stand for?

_____

f) What is Tom's title?

_____

g) What is another term for Christian name?

_____

h) What is another term for surname?

_____

i) Give an example of a nickname of someone you know.

_____

GRAMMAR

Present Simple or Present Continuous?

5 Complete the following text. Use the Present Simple or Present Continuous.

Sally is quite an average 16-year-old. She (1 *go*) _____ to a comprehensive school near her home where she (2 *study*)_____ for her exams. Then she hopes to train to be a secretary, but her mother (3 *say*)_____ she would prefer her to stay on at school for another two years. In her spare time she (4 *play*) _____ tennis and she likes swimming. She (5 *not have*)_____ a boyfriend at the moment because she (6 *like*)_____ going around with a lot of different people. Like her friends, Sally (7 *wear*)_____ jeans and pullovers in her free time but at school she

has to wear a uniform. At the moment she (8 *prefer*)_____ to stay at home and watch television because she (9 *save*) _____ money to go on holiday and (10 *not want*)_____ to spend a lot on going out.

How often...?

6   Answer the questions using expressions like the ones in the box.

> once/twice/three/four times a...
> once every...   every...   every other...

a) How often does a weekly magazine come out?
   Once a week.

b) How often do you have a birthday?

_____

c) How often is there a leap year?

_____

d) How often do you have elections or change the Government in your country?

_____

e) How often do you think it rains in England during the summer?

_____

f) How often is the post delivered in your country?

_____

g) How often do you eat vegetables?

_____

7   The following words are in the wrong order. Make sentences, paying special attention to where adverbs of frequency go. Add any other words that are necessary and change the verbs into the correct form.

a) always / bed / 10 p.m. / go / he
   He always goes to bed at 10 p.m.

b) usually / food / buy / supermarket / we

_____

_____

c) watch / TV / often / they / evening

_____

_____

d) early / weekend / never / they / get up

_____

_____

e) cinema / frequently / winter / go / I

_____

_____

f) be / afternoon / she / always / tired

_____

_____

g) church / sometimes / Sundays / Judith / go

_____

_____

WRITING

Punctuation

8   Punctuate the following sentences, using capital letters where necessary.

a) what is it

_____

b) i work in an office and i need to think that people have some respect for me

_____

_____

c) im liz at the moment im wearing a suit

_____

_____

d) i look better that way she said

_____

_____

e) its because im wearing johns shoes

_____

_____

f) you look a dreadful sight

_____

Dictation

9   [▭ 2.1]   Listen to Mrs Roberts's phone call to her son, Michael as many times as you like and complete the gaps. Check your spelling carefully.

'Hello, Michael ... Yes, we're in Portugal. _____

_____

near the beach ... Dad? Oh, _____

_____ the pool sunbathing ... Yes,

_____ enormously.

_____ suntan.

_____ very much ...

Well, _____

_____,

but not often. By the way, _____

_____ your new job? ... Great!

And what _____?

... Really! ... Well, see you soon, then ... Bye.'

Adventures abroad

READING

1 Read the text. Then look at the items below and write a sentence for each to say how they are important to the story.

a) Karine *Karine was Susanna's sister-in-law and*
   she and Gayaney were visiting her when the
   earthquake happened.

b) a black dress

c) a jar of jam
d) broken glass
e) an Arctic explorer
f) boxes of apples and bottles of lemonade

Earthquake Ordeal for Mother and Child

The Armenian earthquake continues to produce stories of bravery, like that of Susanna Petrosyan, a 26-year-old mother, who was buried alive for over a week with her four-year-old daughter, Gayaney, after a building collapsed on top of them.

On the morning of the earthquake Susanna's husband drove Gayaney and her mother to his sister Karine's apartment. Susanna wanted to try on a black dress that Karine had for sale. It fitted perfectly. As she was taking it off, the fifth floor apartment began to tremble and then shake violently. Still wearing only her underwear, Susanna grabbed Gayaney and ran to the door with her. As she opened the door the floor opened under their feet and the nine-floor apartment collapsed. The three of them fell into the basement.

Trapped on her back in the dark Susanna felt around and found a jar of blackberry jam and, on the second day, after Karine died, she gave it to Gayaney to eat. However, as the days passed Gayaney began to plead for something to drink. Susanna had no water or other liquids and she thought her daughter was going to die of thirst. Then she remembered a television programme about an explorer in the Arctic who was dying of thirst and who was saved by drinking his friend's blood. She found a piece of broken glass, cut her finger and gave her daughter her blood to suck. Because of the bitter cold, Susanna felt no pain.

'I knew I was going to die,' Susanna said. 'But I wanted my daughter to live.'

She began to hallucinate. When she closed her eyes and opened them again she thought she could see boxes full of apples and bottles of lemonade.

On December 14th, the eighth day of their captivity, Russian rescue workers opened a small hole near them, letting a shaft of light into their prison.

'We're saved!' Susanna remembers crying.

Mother and daughter were airlifted to a hospital 60 miles away. For four days they were both in intensive care but now they are fully recovered.

2 Write down the questions which correspond to these answers, based on the text.

a) 'Where _____?'
'On the fifth floor of an apartment block.'

b) 'What _____?'
'She was taking off the dress.'

c) 'What _____?'
'She grabbed Gayaney and went to the door.'

d) 'What _____?'
'The building collapsed.'

e) 'How long _____?'
'For eight days.'

f) 'Who _____?'
'Some Russian workers.'

Vocabulary in context

3 Match these verbs from text (a–e) with their dictionary definitions (1–5) as follows. First look carefully at the text to find the context of the word, and then choose the correct definition.

a) *buried* (line 3)   _____
b) *collapsed* (line 5)   _____
c) *fitted* (line 9)   _____
d) *tremble* (line 11)   _____
e) *hallucinate* (line 31) _____

1 *v* to see things which are not there
2 *v* to push deep into or under
3 *v* to be the right size or shape for
4 *v* to move backwards or forwards or from side to side
5 *v* to fall down or inwards suddenly

VOCABULARY

Countries and nationalities

4 Complete the following chart. Use your dictionary to mark where the stress should be.

Country	Nationality
'China	*Chin'ese*
'Turkey	_____
_____	'Spanish
_____	Au'stralian
_____	'German
Bra'zil	_____
_____	Japa'nese
'Finland	_____
_____	'Welsh
Al'geria	_____
_____	E'gyptian

Family relationships

5 Use the family tree to fill in the gaps in the sentences.

Ross m Virginia
Carol m Dennis   Jack   Phil m Katharine
Andy m Liz   Sally   Bill
Nick   Tina

a) Bill is Phil and Katherine's _____.

b) Nick and Tina are Carol and Dennis's _____.

c) Andy and Liz are Nick and Tina's _____.

d) Katharine is Ross and Virginia's _____.

e) Dennis is Jack's _____.

Spelling

6 [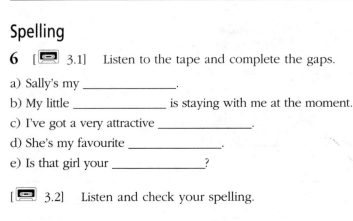 3.1]   Listen to the tape and complete the gaps.

a) Sally's my _____.

b) My little _____ is staying with me at the moment.

c) I've got a very attractive _____.

d) She's my favourite _____.

e) Is that girl your _____?

[🔊 3.2]   Listen and check your spelling.

GRAMMAR

Time expressions

7   Complete the gaps below with one of the following expressions: *while, in, at, for, on, during.*

a) He was playing tennis _____*on*_____ Sunday afternoon _____ it was raining.

b) I get up _____ seven o'clock _____ the morning.

c) She lived _____ France _____ twenty years.

d) I make sure all the doors are locked _____ night.

e) We're going on holiday _____ 10th July.

f) _____ the day I usually eat a snack.

Talking about the past: *used to*

8   Complete the sentences below appropriately, using *used to.*

a) Nowadays this town is very busy but *it used to be very quiet.*

b) I _____ a cat, but it died.

c) _____ have a computer when you were a child?

d) Petrol _____ very cheap but now it costs a fortune!

e) I didn't _____ cheese but I love it now.

Irregular Past Simple forms

9   Write down the Past Simple forms of the following irregular verbs.

Base form	Past Simple
think	*thought*
find	_____
shake	_____
fall	_____
say	_____
cut	_____
run	_____
give	_____
drive	_____
begin	_____
feel	_____

Pronunciation of Past Simple forms

10   Put the Past Simple forms of the regular verbs in the box into one of the columns below, according to the pronunciation of the endings.

> collapsed   rescued   wanted   saved   trapped
> closed   fitted   died   lifted   grabbed   pleaded
> passed   hoped

/t/	/d/	/ɪd/
collapsed	_____	_____
_____	_____	_____
_____	_____	_____
_____	_____	_____

Past tenses and linkers

11   Look at the picture composition below. Change the verbs to
the Past Simple or the Past Continuous and fill in the other gaps
with one of the linking words in the box in order to complete
the story.

| while | finally | and | although | however | as soon as | but | then | before | when |

The Unlucky Burglar

One evening Paul (1 *watch*)_____ the television (2)_____ (3 *eat*)_____
his supper (4)_____ the door suddenly (5 *open*)_____ and a burglar
(6 *come*)_____ in. He (7 *wear*)_____ a mask and (8 *carry*) _____ a sack.
(9)_____ doing anything else he (10 *tie*)_____ Paul to the chair.
(11)_____ he (12 *go*)_____ upstairs to look for money. (13)_____ he
(14 *not find*)_____ any money he (15 *find*)_____ a lot of jewellery, which he
(16 *put*)_____ into his sack. In his rush to get downstairs he (17 *not see*)_____ the
dog which (18 *lie*)_____ at the bottom of the stairs and he (19 *fall*)_____ over it,
losing his glasses. (20)_____ the burglar (21 *look for*)_____ them, Paul
(22 *try*)_____ to free himself. (23)_____ Paul (24 *manage*)_____ to
escape and he (25 *phone*)_____ the police. (26)_____ the burglar
(27 *find*)_____ his glasses he (28 *run*)_____ out of the house. (29)_____,
unfortunately for him, the police (30 *wait*)_____ for him at the end of the garden.

Home thoughts from abroad

LISTENING

1 [▣ 4.1]   Listen to Sarah and Pam describing how they learnt Italian and German. Write *T* (for *True*) or *F* (for *False*) next to each of the statements.

SARAH

a) When she went to Italy she could already speak a little Italian. _____

b) She found it difficult to communicate at first. _____

c) People did not like her making mistakes. _____

d) Now she is fluent but not very accurate. _____

PAM

a) Pam wasn't completely happy with her classes. _____

b) There wasn't enough conversation practice. _____

c) She studied for four years in Germany. _____

d) She learnt to speak by talking to her German friends. _____

2   Listen again and answer the following questions.

a) How did Sarah try to learn Italian when she first got to Italy?

_____

b) Why was she braver after a month?

_____

_____

c) In what ways was Pam's first German class traditional?

_____

_____

d) What kind of German classes did she have at university?

_____

Free writing

3   On a separate piece of paper write about your experiences of learning a foreign language. For example, you might like to talk about how you learnt (e.g. in a class, from a book); what was easy; what was difficult, any problems you had; how you made progress.

GRAMMAR

Past Simple or Present Perfect?

4 Underline the most likely form of the verb in each sentence.

a) When they lived in Morocco they *ate / have eaten* in restaurants every day.

b) She *only went / 's only been* to a hypnotist once in her life.

c) *Did you go / Have you been* to the opening night of 'Miss Saigon' last week?

d) I *watered / have watered* the plants yesterday.

e) Your mother *telephoned / has telephoned* while you were out.

f) I *heard / 've heard* that record. Put something else on.

g) When *did you hear / have you heard* it?

h) He *met / 's met* Judi Dench last week.

i) I *never went / 've never been* on Concorde. I'd like to.

j) *Did you ever have / Have you ever had* malaria before?

5 Make sentences from these groups of words. Put the verbs in the Past Simple or the Present Perfect, using the time expressions in brackets.

a) live / Indonesia? (*ever*)

_____

b) play golf? (*yesterday*)

_____

c) meet my wife / Poland (*ten years ago*)

_____

_____

d) have / cup of coffee (*already*)

_____

_____

e) plane / not leave (*yet*)

_____

f) see any good films? (*recently*)

_____

_____

g) Kay / not phone / mother (*last week*)

_____

_____

h) visit / Paris (*never*)

_____

Been or gone?

6 Write *been* or *gone* in the gaps.

a) There you are! Where have you _____?

b) 'Where's Brita?' 'Oh, she's _____ out.'

c) All the money's _____. Who's taken it?

d) Have you ever _____ to Russia?

e) 'Has the doctor _____ yet?' 'No, he's still upstairs.'

Question tags

7 Put a tag at the end of each question.

a) You can drive, ___*can't you*___ ?

b) You haven't been to Syria, _____?

c) He comes from Japan, _____?

d) I'm wonderful, _____?

e) It's never too late, _____?

f) Sue broke your computer, _____?

g) He loves you, _____?

h) We can't go down this street, _____?

i) There's nobody in there, _____?

j) They've taken everything, _____?

k) They're asleep, _____?

l) Give me that watch, _____?

VOCABULARY

Living in Britain

8   Which of the places in the box below would you go to for the following?

a) to buy a magazine _a newsagent's_   f) to borrow some money to buy a house _____

b) to buy a book   _____   g) to buy a bottle of wine   _____

c) to buy fresh meat _____   h) to borrow a book   _____

d) to get medicine   _____   i) to buy some expensive cheese   _____

e) to buy a jacket   _____

> chemist's   building society   delicatessen   off-licence
> newsagent's   bookshop   butcher's   library   boutique

American English

9   Listed below are American English terms for some of the places in the box in the last exercise. What do they correspond to in British English?

a) bookstore   _bookshop_

b) savings and loan association _____

c) liquor store   _____

d) news dealer   _____

e) pharmacy   _____

10   Find in the word puzzle the British English words for the American English words in the box below. Some are written from top to bottom and some are left to right. The first letter of the British English word is given in brackets.

> faucet (*T*)   cookies (*B*)   stove (*C*)
> apartment (*F*)   elevator (*L*)   pants (*T*)
> truck (*L*)   gas (*P*)

P	F	L	A	T	B	H	K
G	S	A	W	R	X	P	I
M	L	C	O	O	K	E	R
B	I	S	C	U	I	T	S
T	F	W	L	S	N	R	Y
A	T	O	Z	E	N	O	Q
P	L	O	R	R	Y	L	V
F	J	Q	N	S	O	U	W

WRITING

Dictation

11   [🔊 4.2]   Listen as many times as you like and complete the first line of these dialogues.

a) '_____' 'Yes, I have.'

b) '_____' 'So have I.'

c) '_____' 'At 6 o'clock.'

d) '_____' 'To catch a train.'

e) '_____' 'Oh, were you?'

A bit windy

READING

1 The Sahara is the large desert in North Africa. Read the text and indicate with a tick which of the sentences below is the best summary. The extract is about:

a) a film in which cotton came down from the sky. _____
b) a misunderstanding about what snow is. _____
c) the differences between Poland and Africa. _____

The fire stood between us and linked us together. A boy added wood and the flames rose higher, illuminating our faces.
'What is the name of your country?'
'Poland.'
Poland was far away, beyond the Sahara, beyond the sea, to the north and the east. The Nana repeated the name aloud. 'Is that how it is pronounced?' he asked.
'That's the way,' I answered. 'That's correct.'
'They have snow there,' Kwesi said.
Kwesi worked in town. Once, at the cinema, there was a movie with snow. The children applauded and cried merrily 'Anko! Anko!' asking to see the snow again. The white puffs fell and fell.
'Those are lucky countries,' Kwesi said. 'They do not need to grow cotton; the cotton falls from the sky. They call it snow and walk on it and even throw it into the river.'

(from *The Snow in Ghana* by Ryszard Kapuściński)

2 Underline the correct alternatives below.

a) The event took place in *Poland/Africa*.

b) The boy lived *south and west / north and east* of Poland.

c) The narrator was *Polish/African*.

d) It was *daytime/nighttime*.

e) The children *had never seen / had seen* real snow.

f) The children *think / do not think* that snow is cotton.

GRAMMAR

Will or going to?

3   Put the verb into the correct form, using *will* or *going to*.

a) A: What time does this train get to Edinburgh?

   B: Don't worry. I'm sure we (*be*)_____ there on time.

b) A: Somebody told me you (*write*)_____ a book.

   B: Yes. I (*send*)_____ you a copy when it's published.

c) A: Oh no. I'm late for work.

   B: Hang on a minute and I (*give*)_____ you a lift.

d) A: What are you buying?

   B: Paint. I (*paint*)_____ the front door.

   A: What colour (*you paint*)_____ it?

   B: I'm not sure. Pink, maybe. Do you think it (*look*)_____ OK?

e) A: Look at those dark clouds!

   B: Yes, it looks as if it (*snow*)_____.

Will or shall?

4   Use *will* or *shall* to write a sentence for each of the following situations.

a) Promise to phone your mother later.   *I'll phone you later, Mum.*_____

b) Suggest to your friend that you go Christmas shopping next week. _____

_____.

c) Ask your brother to lend you his new pullover. _____.

d) Offer to get some drinks in the pub. _____.

e) Refuse to repeat what you said again. _____.

Verbs and prepositions

5   Complete the gaps below with a preposition. Use your dictionary to check your answers.

> **borrow** /'bɒrəʊ/ *v* **1** (**from**) to take or receive something for a certain time and with intention to return: *He borrowed a book from the library.*

a) I borrowed a pen _____*from*_____ my teacher.

b) She is someone that we all depend _____.

c) I wasn't laughing _____ him.

d) When I arrived she was listening _____ the radio.

e) The dog died _____ old age.

f) They never talk _____ each other.

g) I must congratulate you _____ your promotion.

h) Does this book belong _____ you?

i) What do you spend all your money _____?

j) You remind me _____ my mother.

VOCABULARY

Weather: temperature

6 Change the words according to the part of speech in brackets.

a) sun _____sunny_____ (adjective)

b) freeze _____ (adjective)

c) hot _____ (verb)

d) damp _____ (verb)

e) storm _____ (adjective)

f) shower _____ (adjective)

g) ice _____ (adjective)

Telephone expressions

7 Use words from the box to complete the following instructions for how to use a public telephone box in Britain.

> code dial operator engaged receiver
> pips ringing answers ring off

First pick up the (1)_receiver____ and then insert your money. Then (2)_____ the number, remembering to put the area (3)_____ in front of the number. You should hear a (4)_____ tone before somebody (5)_____. You may hear the (6)_____ tone, in which case you should try again later. When your money has run out you will hear the (7)_____; either put more money in to continue your call or (8)_____. If you cannot phone direct, call the (9)_____ and ask him or her to connect you.

Same words, different meanings

8 Look at the four definitions of *tap* below. Which meaning is correct in the following context? *She tapped on the window to attract his attention.*

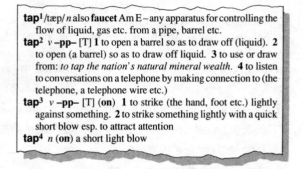

> **tap¹** /tæp/ *n* also **faucet** Am E – any apparatus for controlling the flow of liquid, gas etc. from a pipe, barrel etc.
> **tap²** *v* –pp– [T] **1** to open a barrel so as to draw off (liquid). **2** to open (a barrel) so as to draw off liquid. **3** to use or draw from: *to tap the nation's natural mineral wealth*. **4** to listen to conversations on a telephone by making connection to (the telephone, a telephone wire etc.)
> **tap³** *v* –pp– [T] **(on) 1** to strike (the hand, foot etc.) lightly against something. **2** to strike something lightly with a quick short blow esp. to attract attention
> **tap⁴** *n* **(on)** a short light blow

9 Write down the parts of speech of the words in *italics*. Then guess the meaning of the words and check your answers in the dictionary.

a) The policeman *fined* me for speeding.

b) It was a *fine* day so we went out for a drive.

c) My throat hurt when I *swallowed*.

d) I could see three *swallows* in the trees.

e) My car had a *flat* tyre.

f) It's expensive to rent *flats* in London.

g) I'll give you a *ring* later.

h) She was wearing an emerald *ring*.

PRONUNCIATION

Different words, same pronunciation

10 Tick the pairs of words which have the same pronunciation. Use your dictionary to help you.

> **which** /wɪtʃ/ *determiner, pron* **1** (used in questions, when a choice is to be made) what particular one or

> **witch** /wɪtʃ/ *n* **1** a woman who has magic powers, esp. on who can make bad things happen to people, such as

a) which/witch ✔ g) road/rode _____

b) boot/but _____ h) ear/here _____

c) seat/sit _____ i) know/no _____

d) brake/break _____ j) right/write _____

e) hair/here _____ k) board/bored _____

f) warm/worm _____

Are you 'green'?

LISTENING

1   Look up the words in *italics* in the following sentences using a monolingual dictionary. Mark the stress on the words which have more than one syllable and then write a definition for each of the words in context. (You might also like to write the pronunciation symbols for each word.)

a) *Leaded* petrol is now more expensive than unleaded petrol.
   'leaded: /'ledɪd/ *A kind of petrol* **which has a dangerous chemical added to it.**

b) There is air *pollution* in the city. _____

c) Car *fumes* are very dangerous. _____

d) The animals were covered with *tar*. _____

e) The factories have *ruined* the countryside. _____

2 [▭ 6.1]   Listen to these 10-year-old English children talking about the environment. Match the numbers of the recordings to the statements below.

a) Most people don't know how much we are destroying nature. _3_
b) Children need to take action to protect the environment. _____
c) Unleaded petrol is better for the environment than leaded. _____
d) Technology will be useless when we have destroyed nature. _____
e) Animals are frequently injured by oil. _____

3   Answer these questions according to what the children say.

a) Why is the ozone layer being destroyed? _____

b) How do animals get covered in tar? _____

c) How does Britain's chemical pollution compare with other countries? _____

d) How can young people help? _____

e) Why are living things more important than computers? _____

GRAMMAR

Defining relative clauses

4   Read the example and then write similar definitions for what you see in the pictures.
Example:
An accountant is a person who advises on the use of money.

a) A tightrope walker is _____

_____

_____

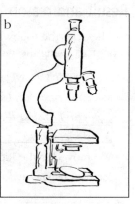

b) A microscope is _____

_____

_____

c) A swan is _____

_____

_____

d) A bank is _____

_____

_____

5   Complete each of these sentences, using a relative clause with *who, which, that, where* or *whose* (where necessary). Choose from the phrases in the box to make your clauses.

a) What's the name of the river *which runs through Florence?* _____

b) The man _____
was Captain Matthew Webb in 1875.

c) That's the town _____.

d) The name of the woman _____
is Alice Walker.

e) What was the name of the restaurant _____?

f) Michelle works for a company _____.

g) What were the names of the children _____?

h) The man _____
lost all his money in the fire.

i) Did you lose that watch _____?

j) *Jaws* was a film about a shark _____.

I gave it to you for your last birthday	he first swam the Channel
his house burnt down	their mother had a skiing accident
it runs through Florence	I was born there
she wrote *The Color Purple*	we went there last week
it attacked and killed many people	it makes computers

Result and reason

6 Rewrite the following in one or two sentences using the words in brackets.

a) As you can't answer that question, I'm going to ask someone else. (*so*)
You can't answer that question so I'm going to ask someone else.

b) We moved to the Ritz because the food in the Metropolis was awful. (*that's why*)

c) Since the English have big gardens they have to spend a lot of time gardening. (*therefore*)

d) My wife is from Senegal. As a result, I am entitled to a Senegalese passport. (*because*)

e) My back feels very painful as I had to lift a lot of heavy boxes at work yesterday. (*as a result*)

f) These birds are very unusual. Therefore, they are protected by law. (*since*)

Clauses of purpose

7 Write a sentence using *so that* or *to* and the phrase in brackets.

a) I am learning English (*better job*).
*I am learning English **so that I can get / to get** a better job.*

b) We have to eat (*live*).

c) I put on a thick scarf (*warm*).

d) We got to the cinema early (*good seats*).

e) The old couple sold their big house (*somewhere smaller in the country*).

f) I wrote to the Prime Minister (*complain / government's environment policy*).

g) The doctor gave him some medicine (*feel better*).

h) She put her hands over her ears (*noise*).

VOCABULARY

Town and country

8   Write *T* (for *Town*) or *C* (for *Country*) next to each of these words. Use a dictionary to help you if necessary.

a) pond   *C*

b) factory   _____

c) field   _____

d) stream   _____

e) skyscraper   _____

f) cow   _____

g) valley   _____

h) roundabout   _____

i) department store _____

j) hay   _____

Adjectives with *-ing* or *-ed*

9   Circle the correct alternative in each of the sentences below.

a) Lilian's very *interesting*/(*interested*) in working in Mexico.

b) We were very *irritating/irritated* to hear they weren't coming.

c) You look as though you've had a very *tiring/tired* day looking after the children.

d) My brother is *terrifying/terrified* of heights.

e) I was very *shocking/shocked* by her appearance.

f) The lesson was deadly *boring/bored*.

g) The results were very *disappointing/disappointed*.

h) That's the most *interesting/interested* idea you've had all day.

WRITING

Semi-formal and personal writing

10   Write the following sentences in a more personal style.

a) I have spoken about this matter on several previous occasions.

_____

_____

b) I must apologise for not sending you the cheque.

_____

_____

c) I would be grateful if you sent me the book I asked for.

_____

_____

d) I visited your parents recently.

_____

_____

Dictation

11   [▭ 6.2]   Listen to the recording as many times as you like and write the conversation.

A: *What are you going to do this evening?*

B: *Oh, I* _____

_____

_____

_____

_____

_____

_____

_____

_____

_____

_____

_____

_____

_____

_____

Choosing a partner

READING

1   Look at this cover of a novel and write down what kind of novel you think it is.

_____

_____

2   Read this extract and write *T* (for *True*) and *F* (for *False*) next to the statements below.

a) Faine fell in love with Burke the first time she met him. _____

b) She stopped seeing him because she was afraid of her feelings. _____

c) Dougal was Faine's fiancé. _____

d) Faine agreed to marry Burke because he loved her. _____

e) Faine wasn't attracted to Burke. _____

f) Burke was jealous of Faine's fiancé.

_____

3   Imagine you are either Burke or Faine. On a separate sheet of paper write a letter to the other person.

a) If you are Burke, ask about Faine's relationship with Dougal.
b) If you are Faine, talk about your relationship with Dougal.

'I don't deserve you,' he whispered shakily, 'but I love you, love you, love you beyond all hope, all reason, all desire.' His hands framed Faine's face, the strong fingers trembling. 'You're so beautiful,' he said, his gaze moving restlessly over her features. 'Strong and beautiful and kind, and there hasn't been a minute since I met you that I haven't thought of you.'

'I thought you were a man who never exaggerated,' she said, smiling because if she didn't she would weep. Turning her head, she kissed the palm of his hand. 'I love you – I have since the second time we met. You kissed me and I wanted you, and then you laughed and my heart melted. I didn't know what had happened to me, but I realised that for my peace of mind I'd better not see any more of you. Nothing like it had ever happened before.'

'Not even with that fool you were engaged to?' Burke demanded quickly, jealously.

'Dougal? Oh no. I tried to convince myself that it was just that I fancied you like mad, but when I found myself agreeing to marry you I realised it had to be love. I knew you weren't in love with me, you see.'

His fingers tightened hurtfully, then he smiled and the pale depths of his eyes warmed. 'The fact that I hated to think of you with a *fiancé* should have warned me that I was in too deep to climb out,' he said huskily.

(from *Mansion for My Love* by Robyn Donald)

VOCABULARY

Adjectives and adverbs

4 Underline all the adjectives and circle all the adverbs in the text in the last section.

5 Complete the following table, using a dictionary where necessary.

ADJECTIVE	ADVERB	NOUN
shaky	shakily	shakiness
		beauty
restless		
	jealously	
deep		
		strength

Relationships

6 Complete the text using words or phrases from the box. Change the verbs into the correct form.

> get married to   propose   bride   fancy   reception   be engaged
> split up   go out   row   ask out

As soon as Somerset set eyes on Melanie at the disco he
(1)_____ her and decided he wanted to
(2 *her*)_____. She accepted his offer and they
(3)_____ together for several months, although they also
argued a lot and (4)_____ a couple of times. On
February 14th, Valentine's Day, he (5)_____ to her and
gave her a beautiful diamond ring. They (6)_____ for
over a year but during this time she met someone else and fell in
love with him. Somerset and Melanie had an enormous
(7)_____ and they decided to separate. A few months
later, Melanie (8)_____ the other man and everybody
said she was a beautiful (9)_____. At the
(10)_____ after the wedding, people were enjoying a
drink when a figure appeared at the back of the room. It was
Somerset …

Parts of the body

7   Label the picture using the words in the box. Use a dictionary if necessary.

> eye palm foot nose ear thigh ankle
> lips shin stomach knee head cheek
> elbow shoulder hand back

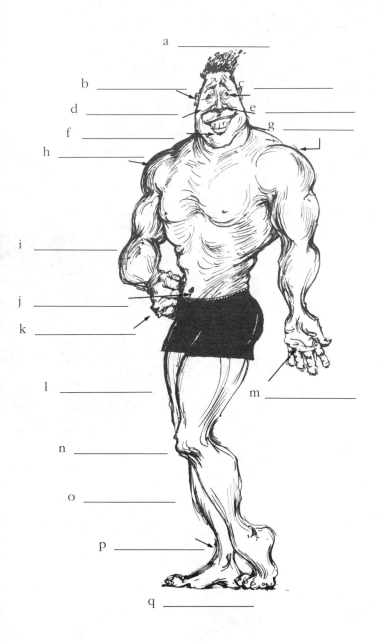

a _____

b _____   c _____

d _____   e _____

f _____   g _____

h _____

i _____

j _____

k _____

l _____   m _____

n _____

o _____

p _____

q _____

8   Match the words in column A to the ones in column B to make compound nouns referring to parts of the body. If necessary use your dictionary to help you. In some cases, there may be more than one possibility.

A	**B**
cheek	style
eye	watch
hair	ache
finger	brow
wrist	lash
ear	nail
stomach	lobe
	bone

9   Match the expressions in group A with the definitions in group B.

A

a) You're nosy. __4__

b) You like pulling someone's leg. ____

c) What a handy person you are. ____

d) Something's on the tip of your tongue. ____

e) You have a chip on your shoulder. ____

f) You put someone's back up. ____

g) You have eyes in the back of your head. ____

h) You put your foot in it. ____

i) You are up to your ears. ____

j) You have your head in the clouds. ____

B

1 You are not quite able to remember something.
2 You are very busy.
3 You are extremely impractical.
4 You are interested in things that don't concern you.
5 You say something wrong and unsuitable.
6 You make playful fun of people.
7 You make someone angry.
8 You are very good at doing useful, practical things.
9 You always feel you are treated unfairly.
10 You see and notice everything.

10 On a separate sheet of paper write one or two sentences about each of the people in the photographs describing their appearance and personality. You might want to use the words in the box.

easy going
lively
bushy
neat
sparkling
straight
curly

Steve

Kate

Winston

Gina

GRAMMAR

Adjective word order

11 Put the adjectives in brackets in the correct order.

a) (*green dark*)

_____ _____ eyes

b) (*old cotton*)

a(n) _____ _____ shirt

c) (*English old delightful*)

a(n) _____ _____

_____ cottage

d) (*leather brown light*)

a _____ _____

_____ jacket

e) (*antique silver beautiful*)

a _____ _____

_____ bracelet

Possessives

12 Underline the correct alternatives.

a) My computer's working. What about *your/ yours*?

b) He's *my/mine* friend. He's been a friend of *my/mine* for ages.

c) There's *my neighbour's cat / the cat of my neighbour*.

d) Jo now has a car *by herself / of hers / of her own*.

e) We know that's *our/ours*. It's got *our/ours* name on it.

f) Give the dog *it's/its/its'* food, will you?

g) Jill is *hers husband's / her husband's / her husbands'* boss.

h) Use *your own / yours own*. Don't use *my/mine*!

i) Laura goes to a *girl's/girls'* school.

j) I like *your/yours* photos but I prefer *their/theirs*.

PRONUNCIATION

Sound and spelling

13 In each of the following the gaps contain a schwa sound (/ə/). Write down the letters which have been missed out.

a) In th_____ theat_____ he's _____ very clev_____ act_____ .

b) P_____haps in fut_____ I'll live _____broad.

c) My doct_____ is very popul_____ .

d) Is your neighb_____ espec_____lly jeal_____s?

e) What _____ delic_____s t_____mato sal_____d!

f) Don't f_____get th_____ pr_____nunciat_____n ex_____cises!

A place to live

LISTENING

1   Match the words in the box with the different types of homes in the photographs.

> a cottage   a semi-detached house
> a terraced house   a bungalow   a block of flats

a) _____

b) _____

c) _____

d) _____

e) _____

2 [🖭 8.1]   Look at the photographs again.

a) Which of these types of homes do you think would be:

the most expensive? _____

_____

the least expensive? _____

_____

b) Listen to the interview with Kevin Moll, an estate agent in a small town in Britain, and see if your guesses were correct.

3   Listen again and answer the following questions on a separate sheet of paper.

a) Do British people prefer to rent or buy their homes?

b) What are the three reasons?

c) What kind of homes do the following people tend to choose: single people; young couples; old people. Why?

d) Give two reasons why old houses are more expensive than new ones.

e) When people are looking for a house what is the most important thing they need to consider?

f) Write down four examples of things that people may look for when buying a house.

g) What is Kevin's ideal house like?

GRAMMAR

Comparison of adjectives and adverbs

4 In each of the following complete the second sentence so that it means the same as the first.

a) Britain isn't as sunny as Spain.

Spain _is sunnier than Britain._

b) French isn't as hard as Chinese.

Chinese is _____

c) Ironing is more boring than cooking.

Cooking isn't _____

d) Chips aren't as healthy as fruit.

Fruit _____

e) Please don't drive so fast.

Please drive _____

f) Nurses don't earn as much as policemen.

Policemen earn _____

Superlatives

5 Complete the sentences with words from the box.

cold valuable fast comfortable dangerous small

a) The cheetah is _the fastest_ animal in the world.

b) A bear is one of _____
animals in the world.

c) The Vatican City is _____
state in the world.

d) The _Mona Lisa_ is _____
painting in the world.

e) Antarctica is _____
continent in the world.

f) A Rolls-Royce is one of _____
cars in the world.

Prepositions of place

6 Complete the sentences with words from the box.

against   above   in front of   under   in   by   below

a) It's no use hiding ___under___ the bedclothes.

b) He lives on the top floor and Charles lives on the one _____.

c) I saw a ladder leaning _____ the wall.

d) The only problem with living in the basement flat is all the noise from _____.

e) We couldn't see the television screen because there was a bookcase _____ it.

f) The children's toys were kept _____ the corner _____ the window.

Prepositions of direction

7 Look at the picture and complete the sentences.

a) The car is going ___round___ the roundabout.

b) The man is walking _____ the zebra crossing.

c) The motorist is driving _____ the traffic lights.

d) The woman is walking _____ the bank.

e) The boy is coming _____ the shop.

f) The cyclist is riding _____ the street.

g) The lorry is driving _____ the bridge.

h) The bus is going _____ the school.

i) The dog has run _____ the hotel.

VOCABULARY

Furniture and household objects

8   Fill in the gaps below to make the names of objects found in the home.

a) You hang your clothes up in it in the bedroom. (_ _ r _ r _ b _)

b) You have them on the bed.
(_ i _ _ _ w s)

c) You sit on it in the living room. (_ o _ a)

d) You wash dishes in it in the kitchen.
(s _ n _)

e) You keep clothes in it in your bedroom.
(c _ e _ t of _ r _ w _ r s)

f) You use it for drying yourself. (t _ _ e _)

Doing things in the house

9   Match the verbs in column A with the nouns they are usually associated with in column B. For some there is more than one possibility.

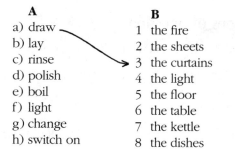

A	**B**
a) draw	1 the fire
b) lay	2 the sheets
c) rinse	3 the curtains
d) polish	4 the light
e) boil	5 the floor
f) light	6 the table
g) change	7 the kettle
h) switch on	8 the dishes

Forming adjectives

10   Make adjectives from the words in brackets.

a) The City is the ____*financial*____ centre of London. (*finance*)

b) She has a _____ approach to working. (*system*)

c) There are _____ trains. (*hour*)

d) It was a very _____ present. (*use*)

e) My car was quite _____. (*rely*)

f) He was an _____ man. (*ambition*)

g) The police said it was a _____ offence. (*crime*)

h) She is a _____ musician. (*talent*)

i) Give me _____ example. (*specify*)

Prefixes

11   Use the prefixes in the box to make words to replace the phrases in *italics*.

un-   re-   mis-   over-

a) He *didn't hear correctly* what I said.
   He **misheard** what I said._____

b) The door was locked so she *opened it with a key.*

   _____

c) You'll have to *write it again.*

   _____

d) He *charged me too much* for a packet of cigarettes.

   _____

e) She *pronounced* the word *incorrectly.*

   _____

f) The steak was *cooked too much* – it was nearly burnt.

   _____

WRITING

Linking expressions

12   Complete the gaps in the sentences with one of the linking expressions from the box. Pay special attention to the punctuation.

because   while   although   so   after
however

a) He forgot to water the plants while she was on holiday _____*so*_____ they all died.

b) It began to get foggy _____ we were coming down the mountain.

c) _____ I had watched the news I switched the TV off.

d) I don't like her much. _____, she is very intelligent.

e) _____ they were so expensive I could only afford to buy one.

f) They decided to go to Italy _____ neither of them spoke a word of Italian.

Reading the signs

READING

1 Underline which of these alternatives might be correct according to superstition.

a) When you see a new moon you should *light a match / bow and turn over the money in your pocket.*

b) When you visit a friend in hospital you should *take cut flowers / take a potted plant.*

c) On the day of your wedding you should *not see your partner before the ceremony / eat the right food.*

d) When someone dies you should *open the doors and windows of the room / carry the person upstairs.*

Read the text and check your answers.

2 Answer the following questions.

a) Why must newborn babies be carried upstairs?

_____

_____

_____

b) When do babies get unwanted birthmarks?

_____

_____

c) When do fairies harm people?

_____

d) What did the numbers 3 and 4 represent?

_____

e) Why was lighting three people's cigarettes from one match dangerous?

_____

_____

_____

_____

Many scholars believe that our superstitions were once part of ancient religions. Common examples of superstitions are throwing salt over the left shoulder after accidentally spilling some, bowing to the new moon while turning over the money in our pocket or purse, avoiding walking under a ladder, and saying 'Bless you!' when someone sneezes.

Some superstitions come from the belief that similar actions produce similar results. Many people believe that a newborn baby must be carried upstairs before being carried downstairs. This is to make sure the child rises in the world and has a successful life. Others believe that a sick person should be given a potted plant instead of cut flowers. A live plant represents hope for the patient's recovery, but cut flowers soon die.

Many superstitions are related to important events in our lives, such as birth, entering adulthood, marriage, pregnancy, and death. They ensure that we pass safely from one stage of our life to the next. For example, a person born on a Sunday will always have good luck. A bride and groom will have bad luck if they see each other on their wedding day before the ceremony. A pregnant woman must eat the right food, or she will give her child an unwanted birthmark. After a person dies, the doors and windows of the room should be opened so the spirit can leave.

We can only guess about the origin of most superstitions. For instance some people think that wearing the colour green is unlucky. This could be because green was supposed to be the colour worn by the 'little people', or fairies, and for a person to wear it would make the fairies jealous and so likely to do the wearer harm. The number 7 may be unlucky because it is the sum of 3 and 4, which are numbers that many ancient peoples associated with male and female. Many people believe that the more modern superstition that lighting cigarettes for three people from one match will bring bad luck comes from the First World War. At night, a match that stayed lit long enough to light three cigarettes gave a target for the enemy.

Whatever their origin, superstitions will probably be with us all the time people fear each other and are uncertain about the future.

GRAMMAR

Open conditionals

3   Complete the following sentences, using the cues in brackets.

a) If you stand out in the rain, _you'll get a cold._ _____ (*a cold*)

b) Unless you wear your glasses, _____ (*ruin your eyesight*)

c) I'll buy you a dog if _____ (*promise, look after*)

d) Unless you tell me everything, _____ (*angry*)

e) Unless _____ (*pay rise*), I refuse to stay in this job.

f) If _____ (*Argentina*), will you send me a postcard?

g) Will you give her the news if _____ ? (*see*)

h) If I get out of prison next year, _____ (*job*)

i) Next holiday, we'll stay at home unless _____ (*cheap flight*)

j) If you give us more homework, _____ (*not do it*)

k) You can't be a translator unless _____ (*improve English*)

Asking questions

4   Your friend has suddenly decided to go to Madrid for the weekend. Make questions to ask him/her, using the cues provided.

a) leave the car / car park full
Where _will you leave the car if the car park's_ _full?_

b) get into the centre of Madrid / no taxis at the airport
How _____
_____ ?

c) not afford the hotels / stay
If _____ ,
where _____ ?

d) eat / run out of money
How _____
_____ ?

e) rains all weekend / do
If _____ ,
what _____ ?

f) get home / miss the plane on Sunday
When _____
_____ ?

Certainty and possibility

5   Rewrite the sentences below according to the word in brackets. Use words like *will*, *may*, *might*, *could* and *probably*.

a) This theatre will have to close. (*Likely*)
    This theatre will probably have to close.

b) It'll snow before the New Year. (*Unlikely*)
    _____
    _____

c) I might go to Brazil. (*Likely*)
    _____

d) Try again! Next time you'll probably succeed. (*Possible*)
    _____
    _____

e) He'll lose his job. (*Unlikely*)
    _____

f) I think Greg might be a good pianist one day. (*Certain*)
    _____

g) Francis is at work. (*Possible*)
    _____

VOCABULARY

Health

6 Underline the correct alternatives.

a) PATIENT: I've got this terrible pain in my chest.

   DOCTOR: I'm afraid you might be very (*ill*/*sick*).

b) PATIENT: I cut myself badly yesterday.

   DOCTOR: Let's have a look at the
   (*wound*/*injury*).

c) PATIENT: I've pulled a muscle in my left leg.

   DOCTOR: Where does it (*hurt*/*wound*)?

d) PATIENT: I've got a (*painful*/*sore*) throat.

   DOCTOR: You've got an (*infection*/*disease*) in
   your throat.

e) PATIENT: When I woke up I had a
   (*fever*/*temperature*).

   DOCTOR: You've probably got a cold coming on.
   I'll give you a (*prescription*/*note*).

Synonyms

7 The words in *italics* are used incorrectly.
Write the correct synonym for each word.

a) I can't eat food which is too *wealthy*.

   _____rich_____

b) My car is very difficult to *begin* in the mornings.

   _____

c) She's a very *high* person. _____

d) He's a very *antique* friend of mine.

   _____

e) What a lovely *stink*! _____

f) Would you *enjoy* a drink? _____

g) Columbia won the match three *nought*.

   _____

h) He went to Dallas on a business *voyage*.

   _____

Antonyms

8 Write down the opposite of the word in *italics*.

a) *rough* winds _____gentle_____

b) *rough* sea _____

c) *stale* bread _____

d) *poor* health _____

e) *strong* tea _____

f) *strong* smell _____

g) *clear* sky _____

h) *cold* weather _____

PRONUNCIATION

Word stress

9 Mark where the stress falls in these words.

a) 'photograph pho'tographer photo'graphic

b) democracy democratic

c) politics political politician

d) personal personality

e) advertise advertisement

f) organise organisation

g) impossible impossibility

h) economy economical

i) sympathy sympathetic sympathise

A better life?

LISTENING

1 Before you listen to two people talking about what they think life will be like in twenty years time, look at the words and expressions in the box and check the ones you don't know in a dictionary. Make sure you know how to pronounce them and where the stressed syllables are.

| mobile compulsory impoverish drought |

2 [🔊 10.1] Listen and write down which words in the box the speakers use.

a) Keith: _____
_____

b) Jenny: _____
_____

3 Underline the correct alternatives.

Keith

a) There *will/won't* be military service.

b) In twenty years time there'll be *fewer/more* cars.

c) People *like / don't like* having motorways near their houses.

Jenny

a) In the future people *will definitely / may* care more about the environment.

b) It is *possible/impossible* that the environment could be poorer.

c) The 'goodies' *will/may* be more powerful.

GRAMMAR

Time clauses

4 Make sentences from the following groups of words.

a) Before … (*go / give you that novel*)
Before I go I'll give you that novel.

b) When he … (*get up / help you with the ironing*)
_____
_____

c) As soon as I … (*find good job / move house*)
_____
_____

d) Until the world … (*more conscious of ecology / environment in danger*)
_____
_____
_____

e) Unless he … (*drive more carefully / have accident*)
_____
_____

f) Before I … (*decide what to do / speak to Sue*)
_____
_____

If or when?

5 Complete the sentences by using *if* or *when*.

a) The dog always barks _____*when*_____ the postman comes.

b) _____ it rains tomorrow I'll go to work by car.

c) She'll go to university _____ she gets good exam results.

d) _____ he's older he'll settle down.

e) Draw the curtains _____ it gets dark.

f) _____ I get my pay cheque I'll pay you back.

Future forms

6 Barbara is a hairdresser and lives in Scotland. On a separate sheet of paper rewrite from the notes below the letter she wrote to her friend Ruth, who lives outside London. Where possible use the Present Continuous or *going to* to talk about the future. Add anything extra as necessary, such as prepositions, articles, etc.

> *Dear Ruth,*
> *Thanks for your letter which arrived yesterday. I am delighted to hear your news and I just thought I'd write and tell you my plans for Christmas.*

a) I / work until 22nd December / when salon close
b) Then we spend Christmas / my family
c) 28th / James and I drive / down to London
d) go to opera in evening / stay the night with my uncle in Wimbledon
e) We / probably / drive down from London / visit you / next morning
f) Anyway / we phone / after Christmas
g) Love to Ben and the baby / (what you call her?)

> *Much love,*
> *Barbara*

Future Passive

7 Put the verb into the correct tense. Use *will* or the present tense and decide which of the verbs are in the passive.

a) Do you think Liverpool (*beat*)___*will be beaten*___ in the match next Saturday?

b) I'm sure the prize (*win*)_____ by that Hungarian novelist.

c) The hostages (*not release*)_____ until the government (*pay*)_____ the kidnappers a million dollars.

d) When you (*retire*)_____ you (*give*)_____ a gold watch.

e) Unless you (*work*)_____ harder you (*fire*)_____

f) If the small animals (*not be*)_____ careful they (*eat*)_____ by the bigger animals.

VOCABULARY

Phrasal verbs with *on* and *off*

8   Phrasal verbs with *on* can sometimes suggest that an action is continuing. Phrasal verbs with *off* can sometimes suggest that an action has stopped. Use the words in the box with either *on* or *off* to produce the equivalent of the words in italics.

> carry   hang   break   call   stay   cut

a) (*Wait a moment.*)_____, I'll be there in a second.

b) They (*cancelled*)_____ the football match because of the snow.

c) Rebecca wants to (*remain*)_____ at school after her exams.

d) The phone was (*disconnected*)_____ because they hadn't paid their bill.

e) Mary decided to (*continue*)_____, in spite of the noise.

f) He decided to (*end*)_____ the relationship.

Phrasal verbs with *take*

9   Look at the dictionary entries for the word *take* and find an equivalent phrasal verb for the words in italics in the sentences below.

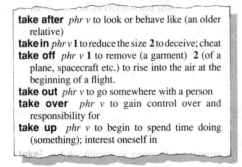

take after *phr v* to look or behave like (an older relative)
take in *phr v* **1** to reduce the size **2** to deceive; cheat
take off *phr v* **1** to remove (a garment) **2** (of a plane, spacecraft etc.) to rise into the air at the beginning of a flight.
take out *phr v* to go somewhere with a person
take over *phr v* to gain control over and responsibility for
take up *phr v* to begin to spend time doing (something); interest oneself in

a) She *removed* her coat because it was too warm. _____

b) The plane *left the ground* on time. _____

c) You *have a lot of your mother's characteristics.* _____

d) I *have taken control of* my father's business. _____

e) David *went* to the cinema *with* Amanda. _____

f) I was completely *deceived* by her lies. _____

Describing objects – size and shape

10   Complete the sentences with words from the box. Use your dictionary if necessary.

rectangle   triangle   circle   cube

a) A _____ is round, like a wheel.

b) A _____ is a block with six equal sides.

c) A _____ has two horizontal sides and two vertical sides.

d) A _____ has three straight sides and three angles.

11   Draw the following in the space below.

a) a square with a diagonal line going from one corner to another
b) two parallel lines
c) a pyramid
d) an oval
e) a straight line
f) a curved line
g) a pointed stick
h) a jagged knife

WRITING

Spelling

12   Look at this extract from a composition written by a student. The teacher has circled all the spelling mistakes. Correct the mistakes using your dictionary to help you if necessary.

experiences

I always have bad (expiriences) when I travel by car. In (Februry) I (desided) to go and visit my (neice) in Birmingham because it was her twenty-first birthday (Unfortunatly) the trains were on strike all that week (wich) meant it was (neccesary) to go by car. (Siting) behind a wheel in traffic jams for (ours) on end is not my idea of fun, and (especialy) when the (whether) is awful – it was foggy and (poring) down all the way. It was a great (releif) when I eventually arrived.

Is the service good enough?

LISTENING

Before listening

1   Where do you go to:

a) buy a stamp?   *a post office*

b) have a haircut?   _____

c) book a holiday?   _____

d) have your clothes cleaned? _____

e) get your watch mended?   _____

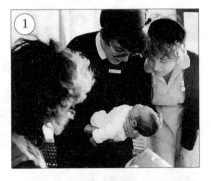

2   Match the descriptions to the photographs and the words in the box.

| plumber   midwife   vet   optician   mechanic |

a) Someone who tests your eye sight. *3 – an optician*

b) Someone who treats sick animals. _____

c) Someone who repairs water pipes. _____

d) Someone who fixes your car.   _____

e) Someone who delivers babies.   _____

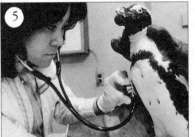

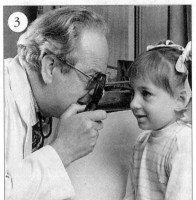

Listening

3   [🔲 11.1]   Listen to the recordings and match them to the places or people referred to in the last two exercises.

a) _____   d) _____

b) _____   e) _____

c) _____

4   For each recording make notes about the conversation on a separate sheet of paper. Example:

a) Patient having eyes tested. Bad eyesight. Needs new contact lenses.

FUNCTIONS

Requesting and asking permission

5 Continue the lines of dialogue below. Remember to use an expression appropriate to the situation.

a) You stop a stranger in the street and ask the time.

Excue me. Sorry to trouble you. Could you tell _me the time, please?_

b) Your best friend is looking after your flat while you are away. Tell him/her what to do. For example, water the plants and feed the fish.

_____

_____

_____

c) You want to miss a class next week. Ask your teacher's permission, giving a reason.

_____

_____

_____

d) You have lost your cat. You see your friend in the street and ask him/her to help you look for it.

_____

_____

_____

e) You have a new boss. You want to take July and August as holiday. Ask permission, giving a reason.

_____

_____

_____

f) Every day the same passer-by drops litter in your garden. You ask him/her to stop.

_____

_____

_____

_____

Apologising and making excuses

6 Match the sentences in group A with the responses in group B.

A

a) 'Would you like me to give you a lift?' __6__

b) 'Could you possibly tell me where the nearest bank is?' _____

c) 'I don't suppose I could move nearer the front, could I?' _____

d) 'What would you like to drink?' _____

e) 'Do you think you could stop biting your nails?'

_____

f) 'Get me the British Council in Madrid, will you?'

_____

g) 'Could I see the doctor this afternoon?' _____

h) 'Try the blue one on.' _____

B

1 'I'll try but I'm very tense at the moment.'
2 'I do apologise but there are no other seats left.'
3 'No. I'm afraid blue doesn't suit me. I'll take the red one.'
4 'Nothing, thanks. I'm driving.'
5 'Terribly sorry, but he's not in until tomorrow morning.'
6 'No, it's all right thanks. I've got a return train ticket.'
7 'I'm so sorry. I'm a stranger here myself.'
8 'I'm afraid the number's engaged.'

VOCABULARY

Adjectives into nouns

7 Some common endings of nouns which come from adjectives are: *-th*, *-ance*, *-ence* and *-(i)ty*. Fill in the gaps with the correct noun.

a) Since you've been absent from class your English has got worse.
   Your ____absence____ from class has made your English worse.

b) Who knows whether it's true or not!
   Who knows the _____!

c) It's not important to me.
   It's of no _____ to me.

d) I believe that we are all equal.
   I believe in _____.

e) Since she's lived abroad she's more self-confident.
   Living abroad has increased her _____.

f) How long is this river?
   What's the _____ of this river?

g) The stockmarket was very uncertain about the effect of inflation.
   There was great _____ in the stockmarket about the effect of inflation.

h) Why are Liverpool such a popular football team?
   What's the reason for Liverpool's _____?

8 Write the noun for the adjectives in brackets.

a) People were dying of _____.
   (*hungry*)

b) Salt gives you a _____. (*thirsty*)

c) You can feel the _____ of the fire from here. (*warm*)

d) I've never doubted your _____.
   (*honest*)

e) This computer will improve our _____. (*efficient*)

f) She had a great feeling of _____ when she saw him. (*anxious*)

Cooking

9 Write *A* (cooking with oil), *B* (cooking with water) or *C* (cooking with dry heat) next to each of the following.

a) simmer _____
b) fry _____
c) boil _____
d) bake _____
e) steam _____
f) roast _____
g) poach _____

10 Which of these can you do to:

a) cheese – *melt, grate, peel, slice*?
   _____

b) an onion – *peel, fry, pour, chop*?
   _____

c) an egg – *beat, stir, crack, melt*?
   _____

11 Circle the odd one out in each of the following.

a) knife, teaspoon, teapot, fork
b) saucepan, kettle, tablespoon, frying pan
c) cork, plate, saucer, cup
d) bowl, mug, dish, sieve
e) oven, bin, stove, grill

Key

Key

Unit 1

READING

1

a) *In the morning in Los Angeles* she reads the papers, eats pancakes, gardens and tidies.
In the morning in Britain she has breakfast and cooks.

b) *In the afternoon in Los Angeles* she goes out on her bike, drives into the hills, walks in the forest, eats with friends.
In the afternoon in Britain she walks along the canal, has lunch with family and friends or goes to a pub.

c) *In the evening in Los Angeles* she watches TV or a video.
In the evening in Britain she reads newspapers, has a light meal, watches TV.

2

a) washing up   b) going   c) watching   d) cooking
e) having   f) walking/strolling

3

a) What do you have for breakfast (when you're) in Los Angeles?
b) Where do your parents live?
c) Do you go out in the evenings?
d) What films do you like watching?

4

a) No, they don't.   b) Yes, I am.   c) No, I haven't.
d) Yes, I can.

VOCABULARY

Strong adjectives

5

b) 'filthy   c) de'licious   d) e'normous   e) 'tiny   f) 'furious

Housework

6

b) Sonia is dusting.   d) Peter is sweeping.
c) Steve is ironing.   e) Kate is washing up.

Everyday expressions

7

b) 7   c) 6   d) 1   e) 3   f) 4   g) 5

GRAMMAR

Less direct questions

8

b) … the train leaves?
c) … when / what time the train arrives?
d) … there is a restaurant car …
e) … to buy / I can buy a ticket?

The definite article

9

b) flowers   c) a knife   d) the book
e) children; the children   f) foreign food; Japanese food

So do I / Neither do I

10

b) Neither can he.   e) So does Malcolm's.
c) So have we.   f) Neither is ours.
d) Neither have I.

Unit 2

VOCABULARY

Clothes

1

2 belt	6 overcoat	10 shorts
3 necklace	7 gloves	11 sandals
4 scarf	8 cardigan	12 socks
5 earring	9 bracelet	

Parts of speech

2

Examples:
a) cardigan   b) is wearing   c) white   d) quietly

Jobs

3

b) 'dentist   c) li'brarian   d) 'architect
e) a'ccountant   f) 'plumber   g) elec'trician
h) engi'neer   i) 'lawyer   j) 'surgeon

Names and titles

4

a) Grier
b) AAD
c) Middle names
d) Miss or Mrs
e) The woman is married.
f) Mr
g) First name
h) Family name
i) (A nickname is a name used informally instead of the person's real name.) For example, the footballer Paul Gascoigne is called *Gazza*.

GRAMMAR

Present Simple or Present Continuous?

5

1 goes	6 likes
2 is studying	7 wears
3 says	8 prefers
4 plays	9 is saving
5 doesn't have / hasn't got	10 doesn't want

How often…?

6

Example answers:
b) Once a year.
c) Every four years.
d) Every four or five years.
e) Every other day.
f) Twice a day.
g) Twice a day.

7

b) We usually buy our food at the supermarket.
c) They often watch TV in the evening.
d) They never get up early at the weekend.
e) I frequently go to the cinema in the winter.
f) She is always tired in the afternoon.
g) Judith sometimes goes to church on Sundays.

WRITING

Punctuation

8

a) What is it?

b) I work in an office and I need to think that people have some respect for me.

c) I'm Liz. At the moment I'm wearing a suit.

d) 'I look better that way,' she said.

e) It's because I'm wearing John's shoes.

f) You look a dreadful sight!

Dictation

9

'Hello, Michael … Yes, we're in Portugal. *We're staying at this brilliant hotel* near the beach … Dad? Oh, *he's sitting by* the pool sunbathing … Yes, *he's enjoying himself* enormously. *He's beginning to get a wonderful* suntan. *He says he misses you* very much … Well, *in the evenings he goes out for long walks and sometimes takes me to lovely restaurants,* but not often. By the way, *how are you getting on in* your new job? … Great! And what *do you do at the weekends*? … Really! … Well, see you soon, then … Bye.'

Unit 3

READING

1

b) Susanna was trying on a black dress when the earthquake happened.

c) Susanna found a jar of blackberry jam when they were trapped under the building, and gave it to Gayaney to eat.

d) Susanna cut her finger with broken glass so that her daughter could suck her blood.

e) Susanna remembered a television programme about an Arctic explorer who drank his friend's blood when he was dying of thirst.

f) Susanna imagined she could see these.

2

a) 'Where was Susanna when the earthquake happened?' / 'Where did Karine live?'

b) 'What was Susanna doing when the earthquake happened / when the building began to tremble?'

c) 'What did she do?'

d) 'What happened next?'

e) 'How long were they buried / did they stay there?'

f) 'Who found/rescued them?'

Vocabulary in context

3

a) 2   b) 5   c) 3   d) 4   e) 1

VOCABULARY

Countries and nationalities

4

Country	Nationality
'China	Chi'nese
'Turkey	*'Turkish*
'Spain	'Spanish
Au'stralia	Au'stralian
'Germany	'German
Bra'zil	*Bra'zilian*
Ja'pan	Japa'nese
'Finland	*'Finnish*
'Wales	'Welsh
Al'geria	*Al'gerian*
'Egypt	E'gyptian

Family relationships

5

a) son   b) grandchildren   c) parents   d) daughter-in-law

e) brother-in-law

Spelling

6

a) daughter   b) nephew   c) cousin   d) aunt

e) niece

GRAMMAR

Time expressions

7

a) while   b) at, in   c) in, for   d) at   e) on   f) During

Talking about the past: *used to*

8

b) … used to have …

c) Did you use to have …

d) … used to be …

e) … use to like …

Irregular Past Simple forms

9

Base form	Past Simple form
think	thought
find	*found*
shake	*shook*
fall	*fell*
say	*said*
cut	*cut*
run	*ran*
give	*gave*
begin	*began*
drive	*drove*
feel	*felt*

Pronunciation of Past Simple forms

10

/t /	/d /	/ɪd /
collapsed	*rescued*	*wanted*
trapped	*saved*	*fitted*
passed	*closed*	*lifted*
hoped	*died*	*pleaded*
	grabbed	

Past tenses and linkers

11

1 was watching	11 Then	21 was looking for
2 and	12 went	22 tried
3 eating	13 Although	23 Finally
4 when	14 didn't find	24 managed
5 opened	15 found	25 phoned
6 came	16 put	26 As soon as
7 was wearing	17 didn't see	27 found
8 carrying	18 was lying	28 ran
9 Before	19 fell	29 However
10 tied	20 While	30 were waiting

Unit 4

LISTENING

1
SARAH
a) False   b) True   c) False   d) True
PAM
a) True   b) True   c) False   d) True

2
a) She tried to read the newspapers, went to the cinema and had Italian friends.
b) Because she began to recognise things that people had said and that she had read and felt able to try things out and didn't mind making lots of mistakes.
c) They were given lists of vocabulary to learn and quite a lot of reading followed by answering questions. Very little of the class was in German.
d) It was all translation work.

GRAMMAR

Past Simple or Present Perfect?

4

b) 's only been	g) did you hear
c) Did you go	h) met
d) watered	i) 've never been
e) telephoned	j) Have you ever had
f) 've heard	

5
a) Have you ever lived in Indonesia?
b) Did you play golf yesterday?
c) I met my wife in Poland ten years ago.
d) I've already had a cup of coffee.
e) The plane hasn't left yet.
f) Have you seen any good films recently?
g) Kay didn't phone her mother last week.
h) I've never visited Paris.

Been or gone?

6
a) been   b) gone   c) gone   d) been   e) gone

Question tags

7

b) have you?	h) can we?
c) doesn't he?	i) is there?
d) aren't I?	j) haven't they?
e) is it?	k) aren't they?
f) didn't she?	l) will you?
g) doesn't he?	

VOCABULARY

Living in Britain

8

b) a bookshop	f) a building society
c) a butcher's	g) an off-licence
d) a chemist's	h) a library
e) a boutique	i) a delicatessan

American English

9

b) a building society	d) a newsagent's
c) an off-licence	e) a chemist's

10
faucet (TAP), cookies (BISCUITS), stove (COOKER), apartment (FLAT), elevator (LIFT), pants (TROUSERS), truck (LORRY), gas (PETROL)

```
P  F  L  A  T  B  H  K
G  S  A  W  R  X  P  I
M  L  C  O  O  K  E  R
B  I  S  C  U  I  T  S
T  F  W  L  S  N  R  Y
A  T  O  Z  E  N  O  Q
P  L  O  R  R  Y  L  V
F  J  Q  N  S  O  U  W
```

WRITING

Dictation

11
a) 'Have you ever been to India?'
b) 'She's seen lots of strange places.'
c) 'When did you get in?'
d) 'Where were you going when I saw you?'
e) 'I was talking to my friend over there.'

Unit 5

READING

1
Summary b).

2
a) Africa   b) south and west   c) Polish   d) nighttime
e) had never seen   f) think

GRAMMAR

Will or going to?

3
a) A: we'll be
b) A: you are going to write
   B: I'll send
c) A: I'll give
d) B: I'm going to paint
   A: are you going to paint
   B: it will look
e) B: it's going to snow

Will or shall?

4
b) Shall we go Christmas shopping next week?
c) Will you lend me your new pullover?
d) I'll get some drinks. / Shall I get some drinks?
e) I won't repeat it again!

Verbs and prepositions

5

b) on c) at d) to e) of f) to g) on h) to i) on j) of

VOCABULARY

Weather: temperature

6

b) freezing c) heat d) dampen e) stormy f) showery
g) icy

Telephone expressions

7

2 dial	5 answers	8 ring off
3 code	6 engaged	9 operator
4 ringing	7 pips	

Same word, different meaning

8

tap³: definition 2

9

a) verb b) adjective c) verb d) noun e) adjective
f) noun g) noun h) noun

PRONUNCIATION

10

Words with the same pronunciation:
d) brake/break g) road/rode i) know/no j) right/write
k) board/bored

Unit 6

LISTENING

1

b) po'llution: /pə'luːʃən/ Dirty air.
c) fumes: /fjuːmz/ The gases that are produced by cars.
d) tar: /tɑː/ A black, sticky substance obtained from coal.
e) 'ruined: /'ruːɪnd/ Destroyed.

2

b) 4 c) 1 d) 5 e) 2

3

a) Because car fumes are helping to destroy the ozone layer.
b) When oil tankers spill their oil on the beaches.
c) It is worse.
d) By setting up clubs and doing something about the problems.
e) Because computers have no feelings, unlike living things.

GRAMMAR

Defining relative clauses

4

Example answers:
a) A tightrope walker is a person who walks on a high rope at the circus.
b) A microscope is an instrument which makes small things look larger.
c) A swan is a large white bird which lives on rivers and lakes.
d) A bank is a place which looks after your money / where you can put your money when you want to save it.

5

b) The man who (that) first swam the Channel was Captain Matthew Webb in 1875.
c) That's the town where (in which) I was born / (that) I was born in.
d) The name of the woman who (that) wrote *The Color Purple* is Alice Walker.
e) What was the name of the restaurant (which/that) we went to / where we went last week?
f) Michelle works for a company which (that) makes computers.
g) What were the names of the children whose mother had a skiing accident?
h) The man whose house burnt down lost all his money in the fire.
i) Did you lose that watch (which/that) I gave to you for your last birthday?
j) *Jaws* was a film about a giant shark which/that attacked and killed many people.

Result and reason

6

b) The food in the Metropolis was awful. *That's why* we moved to the Ritz.
c) The English have big gardens. *Therefore* they have to spend a lot of time gardening.
d) *Because* my wife is from Senegal I am entitled to a Senegalese passport.
e) I had to lift a lot of heavy boxes at work yesterday. *As a result*, my back feels very painful.
f) *Since* these birds are very unusual they are protected by law.

Clauses of purpose

7

b) We have to eat so that we can live / to live.
c) I put on a thick scarf to keep warm / so that I could keep warm.
d) We got to the cinema early so that we could get / to get good seats.
e) The old couple sold their big house so that they could buy / to buy somewhere smaller in the country.
f) I wrote to the Prime Minister to complain about the government's environment policy.
g) The doctor gave him some medicine so that he would feel / to make him feel better.
h) She put her hands over her ears so that she wouldn't hear the noise.

VOCABULARY

Town and country

8

b) factory *T* c) field *C* d) stream *C* e) skyscraper *T*
f) cow *C* g) valley *C* h) roundabout *T*
i) department store *T* j) hay *C*

Adjectives with *-ing* or *-ed*

9

b) irritated c) tiring d) terrified e) shocked f) boring
g) disappointing h) interesting

WRITING

Semi-formal and personal writing

10

Example answers:
a) I've talked about this many times before.
b) I'm sorry I didn't send you the cheque.
c) Could you send me the book I asked for?
d) I went round to your mum and dad's not long ago.

Dictation

11

A: What are you going to do this evening?
B: Oh, I expect I'll have dinner in the garden.
A: Not a good idea. They say there's going to be quite a shower later.
B: OK. I won't eat outside then.
A: What'll you do instead?
B: Why are you asking me so many questions? If you must know, Mary's said she's going to come round so perhaps we'll watch a video.
A: That doesn't sound very exciting.

Unit 7

READING

1

It is a 'romantic' novel.

2

a) False   b) True   c) True   d) False   e) False   f) True

VOCABULARY

4

Adjectives: strong, beautiful, kind, pale
Adverbs: shakily, restlessly, quickly, jealously, hurtfully, huskily

5

ADJECTIVE	ADVERB	NOUN
shaky	shakily	shakiness
beautiful	*beautifully*	beauty
restless	*restlessly*	*restlessness*
jealous	jealously	*jealousy*
deep	*deeply*	depth
strong	*strongly*	strength

Relationships

6

1 fancied
2 ask her out
3 went out
4 split up
5 proposed
6 were engaged
7 row
8 got married to
9 bride
10 reception

Parts of the body

7

a) head   b) ear   c) eye   d) cheek   e) nose   f) lips
g) back   h) shoulder   i) elbow   j) stomach   k) hand
l) thigh   m) palm   n) knee   o) shin   p) ankle   q) foot

8

eyebrow, eyelash, hairstyle, fingernail, wristwatch, earlobe, earache, stomachache

9

b) 6   c) 8   d) 1   e) 9   f) 7   g) 10   h) 5   i) 2   j) 3

GRAMMAR

Adjective word order

11

a) dark, green eyes
b) an old, cotton shirt
c) a delightful, old English cottage
d) a light brown, leather jacket
e) a beautiful, antique, silver bracelet

Possessives

12

a) yours
b) my, mine
c) my neighbour's cat
d) of her own
e) ours, our
f) its
g) her husband's
h) your own, mine
i) girls'
j) your, theirs

PRONUNCIATION

Sound and spelling

13

a) In the thea*tre* he's *a* very clev*er* ac*tor*.
b) P*er*haps in fut*ure* I'll live *a*broad.
c) My doc*tor* is very popul*ar*.
d) Is your neighb*our* espe*cially* jeal*ous*?
e) What *a* deli*cious* tomato sal*ad*!
f) Don't f*or*get the pronuncia*tion* ex*er*cises!

Unit 8

LISTENING

1

a) a terraced house
b) a block of flats
c) a cottage
d) a semi-detached house
e) a bungalow

2

b) the most expensive: a cottage
   the least expensive: a flat

3

a) British people generally prefer to buy their homes.
b) i) It is part of the British way of life to buy.
    ii) Renting property is throwing money away.
    iii) Buying is a sound investment.
c) i) Flats: one- or two-bedroom apartments or studio apartments.
    ii) Two-bedroom apartments, small cottages or small houses.
    iii) Small houses or bungalows which are easy to run.
d) i) There are fewer of them so they have rarity value.
    ii) They have more character and are more picturesque.
e) How much they can afford.
f) i) More bedrooms.
    ii) A garden.
    iii) A garage and plenty of parking.
    iv) A garden shed.
g) A sports centre with a small flat attached.

GRAMMAR

Comparison of adjectives and adverbs

4

b) Chinese is *harder than French*.
c) Cooking *isn't as/so boring as ironing*.
d) Fruit *is healthier than chips*.
e) Please drive *more slowly / slower / less fast*.
f) Policemen earn *more than nurses*.

Superlatives

5
b) the most dangerous
c) the smallest
d) the most valuable
e) the coldest
f) the most comfortable

Prepositions of place

6
b) below   c) against   d) above   e) in front of   f) in, by

Prepositions of direction

7
b) across   c) through   d) away from   e) out of   f) down
g) over   h) towards   i) past

VOCABULARY

Furniture and household objects

8
a) wardrobe   b) pillows   c) sofa   d) sink
e) chest of drawers   f) towel

Doing things in the house

9
a) 3   b) 6   c) 8   d) 5   e) 7   f) 1   g) 2
h) 4 or 7

Forming adjectives

10
b) systematic   c) hourly   d) useful   e) reliable
f) ambitious   g) criminal   h) talented   i) specific

Prefixes

11
b) unlocked it   c) rewrite it   d) overcharged me
e) mispronounced   f) overcooked

WRITING

Linking expressions

12
b) while   c) After   d) However   e) Because   f) although

Unit 9

READING

1
a) … bow and turn over the money in your pocket.
b) … take a potted plant.
c) … not see your partner before the ceremony.
d) … open the doors and windows of the room.

2
a) Newborn babies must be carried upstairs to make sure the child rises in the world and has a successful life.
b) A baby can get unwanted birthmarks if the mother does not eat the right food before the baby's birth.
c) Fairies harm people if people wear green and make the fairies jealous.
d) The numbers 3 and 4 represent male and female.
e) Lighting three people's cigarettes from one match was dangerous because in the First World War a match which stayed lit long enough to light three cigarettes gave a target to the enemy.

GRAMMAR

Open conditionals

3
b) … you'll ruin your eyesight.
c) … you promise to look after it.
d) … I'll get/be very angry.
e) … you give me a pay rise, …
f) … you go to Argentina, …
g) … you see her.
h) … I'll get a job.
i) … we can get a cheap flight.
j) … we won't do it.
k) … you improve your English.

Asking questions

4
b) How will you get into the centre of Madrid if there are no taxis at the airport?
c) If you can't afford the hotels, where will you stay?
d) How will you eat if you run out of money?
e) If it rains all weekend, what will you do?
f) When will you get home if you miss the plane on Sunday?

Certainty and possibility

5
b) It probably won't snow before the New Year.
c) I'll probably go to Brazil.
d) Try again! Next time you may/might/could succeed.
e) He probably won't lose his job.
f) Greg will be a good pianist one day.
g) Francis may be at work.

VOCABULARY

Health

6
a) ill   b) wound   c) hurt   d) sore; infection
e) temperature; prescription

Synonyms

7
b) start   c) tall   d) old   e) smell   f) like   g) nil   h) trip

Antonyms

8
b) calm   c) fresh   d) good   e) weak   f) faint   g) cloudy
h) warm

PRONUNCIATION

Word stress

9
b) de'mocracy   demo'cratic
c) 'politics   po'litical   poli'tician
d) 'personal   perso'nality
e) 'advertise   ad'vertisement
f) 'organise   organi'sation
g) im'possible   impossi'bility
h) e'conomy   eco'nomical
i) 'sympathy   sympa'thetic   'sympathise

Unit 10

LISTENING

2
a) Keith: compulsory (/kəmˈpʌlsəri/), mobile (/ˈməʊbaɪl/)
b) Jenny: drought (/draʊt/), impoverish (/imˈpɒvərɪʃ/)

3
Keith
a) will   b) fewer   c) don't like
Jenny
a) may care   b) possible   c) may be

GRAMMAR

Time clauses

4
b) When he gets up he'll help you with the ironing.
c) As soon as I find a good job I'll move house.
d) Until the world is/becomes more conscious of ecology, the environment will be in danger.
e) Unless he drives more carefully he'll have an accident.
f) Before I decide what to do I'll speak to Sue.

If or *when*?

5
b) If   c) if   d) When   e) when   f) When

Future forms

6
a) I'm working until 22nd December when the salon closes.
b) Then we're spending / going to spend Christmas with my family.
c) On the 28th James and I are driving down to London.
d) We are going to the opera in the evening and then we're staying / going to stay the night with my uncle in Wimbledon.
e) We'll probably drive down from London to visit you the next morning.
f) Anyway we'll phone you after Christmas.
g) Love to Ben and the baby. (What are you going to call her?)

Future passive

7
b) will be won
c) won't be released, pays
d) retire, will be given
e) work, will be fired
f) aren't, will be eaten

VOCABULARY

Phrasal verbs with *on* and *off*

8
a) Hang on   b) called off   c) stay on   d) cut off
e) carry on   f) break off

Phrasal verbs with *take*

9
a) took off
b) took off
c) take after
d) have taken over
e) took Amanda out
f) taken in

Describing objects – size and shape

10
a) circle   b) cube   c) rectangle   d) triangle

11

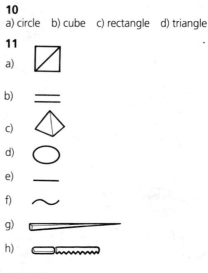
a)
b)
c)
d)
e)
f)
g)
h)

WRITING

Spelling

12
experiences, February, decided, niece, Unfortunately, which, necessary, sitting, hours, especially, weather, pouring, relief

Unit 11

LISTENING

Before listening

1
b) a hairdresser's
c) a travel agent's
d) a cleaner's / a dry-cleaner's
e) a watch-repairer's / a jeweller's

2
b) 5 – a vet (veterinary surgeon)
c) 4 – a plumber
d) 2 – a mechanic
e) 1 – a midwife

Listening

3
a) optician's   b) hairdresser's   c) midwife
d) travel agent's   e) plumber

4
Examples:
b) Customer wants hair dyed. Chooses new colour to try.
c) Mother-to-be in labour. Midwife trying to relax her.
d) Customer wants to have holiday one week earlier than booked. No flight available. Travel agent unable to give refund.
e) Customer asks plumber to fit washing machine / dishwasher. Plumber asks for details and arranges time.

FUNCTIONS

Requesting and asking permission

5

Examples:

b) Please, can you remember to water the plants? Could you remember to feed the fish every day, too?

c) Mr Jones, do you think I could possibly miss the class next week? It's my brother's birthday.

d) Susan, I've lost my cat. You couldn't help me look for it, could you?

e) I'm sorry, Ms Lennard, but would you mind if I took July and August as holiday this year. I know it's a long time but I've got this chance to go to Australia.

f) Excuse me, but would you mind not dropping litter in my garden. It makes an awful mess. How would you like it if I put my litter in your garden?

Apologising and making excuses

6

b) 7   c) 2   d) 4   e) 1   f) 8   g) 5   h) 3

VOCABULARY

Adjectives into nouns

7

b) truth   c) importance   d) equality   e) self-confidence
f) length   g) uncertainty   h) popularity

8

a) hunger   b) thirst   c) warmth   d) honesty   e) efficiency
f) anxiety

Cooking

9

a) B   b) A   c) B   d) C   e) B   f) C   g) B

10

a) melt, grate, slice   c) beat, stir, crack
b) peel, fry, chop

11

b) tablespoon   c) cork   d) sieve   e) bin

PRONUNCIATION

Short and long vowels

12

a) television; ski   c) watch; caught
b) camera; car   d) book; boot

Sound and spelling

13

1 action
2 vest, ready, friend, health
3 build, lift
4 cough, frost
5 couple, cut, trouble, enough, blood

WRITING

14

Example:

WAITER: Good evening, madam. Have you reserved a table?

CUSTOMER: No, I'm afraid not. Could I possibly have a table near the window?

W: Yes, I think so. Come this way, please. Can I take your coat?

C: Thank you. Could I see the menu?

W: Here you are. Would you like something to drink?

C: Yes, could I have a gin and tonic? Oh, and an ashtray please.

W: I'm sorry, madam. The restaurant is no smoking only. Can I take your order?

C: Yes, I'd like …

Unit 12

READING

2

a) The colours manufacturers use for packaging.
The size of a product, which is sometimes deceptive.

b) By paying for expensive research on presentation and for fancy packaging rather than for the product.

3

a) pink (or other pastel colours)
b) green, yellow or brown
c) blue
d) gold or silver
e) blue and white

4

a) True   b) False   c) True   d) False   e) True

5

b) turn(ed) off   c) reaches   d) turned off   e) fancy
f) reach

GRAMMAR

The second conditional

6

b) If I could afford it I'd live in New York.

c) If you practised more you'd be a good musician.

d) If I were young I'd change my job.

e) If I had some time I could help her.

f) If you had a teaching qualification you could work here.

Conditionals and *wish*

7

b) I wish I had a new one.

c) If I were you I'd get another job.

d) I wish I could sell my house.

e) Unless you stop drinking and driving you'll kill yourself.

f) I wish I had time to come (to the party).

Prepositional phrases

8

by car; on business; on television; at work; by accident; in trouble; in hospital; in/on time; at university; on fire; on foot; on the telephone; by mistake; in love; in pencil; at home; by road; at/in/by the cinema

VOCABULARY

Buying

9

a) bargain   b) receipt   c) refund   d) credit card
e) discount   f) half-price

PRONUNCIATION

Vowel sounds

10

/iː/	/e/	/uː/
seen	pen	true
field	*friend*	*lose*
key	says	food

/ɪ/	/ɒ/	/ɜː/
bin	lot	girl
rich	*watch*	*third*
build	cough	word

/æ/	/ʌ/	/ʊ/
cat	cup	book
match	*son*	*could*
hand	blood	put

/ɑː/	/ɔː/
dark	short
heart	*law*
can't	ought

WRITING

Dictation

11

a) Those are only 70p a pound.
b) Yes, a bargain at £1.50 a kilo.
c) OK. Have you got two 20p coins for the meter?
d) I've got a $50 bill and some travellers' cheques. Will that be all right?
e) I can't. This machine only takes £1 coins.
f) Well, it's 2,320 kilometres.
g) 638.

Unit 13

LISTENING

1

flying, menacing, nightmare, classroom, naked, rocks, illness, alive

2

Bonnie's dream: b) i   c) i   d) i
Ben's dream: a) i   b) ii   c) ii
Keith's dream: a) ii   b) i   c) i

3

Bonnie: a)   Ben: a)   Keith: b)

GRAMMAR

Since or *for*?

4

a) since   b) for   c) for   d) since   e) since   f) for

How long...?

5

b) How long has Stuart been teaching English?
c) How long has Di been married to Charles?
d) How long have you and Dick been looking for somewhere else to live?
e) How long have you been sitting on the stairs?
f) How long has she had that job with the BBC?

Present Perfect Simple or Continuous?

6

b) We have been living (have lived) in Nigeria for ten years.
c) The children have been watching television since six o'clock / for three hours.
d) Francis has had that bicycle since last year / for a year.
e) Joanne has been doing her homework since she got home / all evening.
f) She hasn't had a holiday for two years.

Present or Present Perfect?

7

1 don't want
2 have you been
3 've been working
4 don't believe
5 've been doing
6 are you suggesting
7 have you come
8 've been waiting
9 haven't eaten
10 are you shouting
11 do you think
12 've had
13 never want

VOCABULARY

Idiomatic expressions: pairs

8

a) one or two
b) rightly or wrongly
c) free and easy
d) more and more
e) there and then
f) here and there
g) hard and fast
h) short and sweet

WRITING

Summary writing

9

Examples:
1 Different people *need different amounts of sleep.*
2 Energetic people *need more rest but not necessarily more sleep.*
3 There's no point in trying to sleep more *if you you are tense and sleep badly.*
4 It's better to learn to relax *than to take sleeping pills.*
5 Lack of sleep *makes the brain go crazy.*
6 The reason we can't always get to sleep *is anxiety.*
7 If we are angry or stressed *we should try and release our feelings before trying to sleep.*

10

Example summary (98 words):
The important thing about sleep is how well you sleep not how long. Energetic people might not need more sleep but they will certainly need more rest. There's no point in trying to get more sleep if you're tense. It's important to learn to relax and not to depend on such things as sleeping pills. Lack of sleep upsets the brain. We often don't get sleep because we are too busy worrying about what is going to happen to us. If we are angry or stressed it is very important to release these feeling before trying to sleep.

Unit 14

READING

1

a) 4   b) 5   c) 1   d) 7   e) 2   f) 6   g) 3

2

Acting.

3

Words from the text could include: rehearsals; extras; audition; dramatic society; put on productions; walk-on parts; lead (role); lines.

4

a) Being an extra in a film.
b) His local dramatic society.
c) Parts when you don't speak.
d) When he plays the lead role.
e) Learning the lines.
f) No, he thinks he's too old.

VOCABULARY

Synonyms

5

a) free   b) club   c) hard   d) pleasure

Groups of words

6

B   cast (MUSIC)
C   overture (TELEVISION)
D   casserole (GARDENING)

Words often confused

8

b) trip   c) suit   d) miss   e) spilt   f) fun

GRAMMAR

Necessary or not necessary?

9

b) She doesn't have to / needn't get up early.
c) You should/must go.
d) You mustn't/shouldn't drink water from the tap.
e) You must take it.
f) Do I have to / Should I take a present?

Permission and prohibition

10

b) can   c) aren't allowed   d) can't/mustn't
e) mustn't   f) are allowed

Obligation, prohibition and permission (past)

11

2   had to wear
3   did you have to stay
4   had to leave
5   Were you allowed to go out
6   weren't allowed to / couldn't go

PRONUNCIATION

Weak forms

12

b) A: I think they *were* at the cinema last night.
c) A: You turn right *at* the post office.
d) A: I've got a present *for* Tim.
e) B: Yes, I *must* buy him a really nice present.

WRITING

Punctuation and layout

13

63 East St,
Hastings CB2 4XJ
11th February, 1991

Dear Aunt Pat,
I am writing to thank you for the lovely present you sent me. It arrived on Thursday and I've been wearing it all week. It's lovely and warm, so I really appreciate it very much. Isn't the weather horrible and cold at the moment?
I'm sorry that I can't get down to see you this weekend, but if I can I'd like to come another weekend (e.g. the last weekend in this month?).
Anyway, write and tell me if that's all right, and I'll see you soon.
Lots of love,
Mark
PS Have you heard from Janice recently?

Abbreviations

14

a) 6   b) 1   c) 3   d) 8   e) 5   f) 7   g) 4   h) 2

Unit 15

VOCABULARY 1

Food

1

2   half a kilo of fish
3   a bottle of milk
4   a loaf of bread
5   a bag of potatoes
6   a box of chocolates
7   a jar of coffee
8   a bar of chocolate
9   a pot of yoghurt
10   half a dozen eggs
11   a tin of soup
12   a can of coke
13   a piece of cheese
14   a leg of lamb

LISTENING

2

some: spaghetti, sugar, chicken, turkey, fruit, beer, herbal teas (camomile and peppermint)
quite a lot: Chinese food, salads
a lot: broccoli, courgettes, peas
not much/many: beef, pork, fish, Indian tea, alcohol
almost none: food with sugar, spirits, wine, packaged food with additives, food with monosodium glutamate

3

a) … Ed is not very good at cooking it.
b) … it is not supposed to be very good for you.
c) … doesn't eat much fish …
d) … he used to drink gallons of Indian tea.
e) … he eats a lot in summer.
f) … is bad for his skin.
g) … he didn't eat three good meals a day.
h) … he looks at the list of ingredients on packaged food when he goes shopping.

4

a) … eat a lot of …
b) … one of my favourite …
c) … have some …
d) … rarely …

GRAMMAR

Countable or uncountable?

5

Uncountable: b, c, e, g, h

6

a) How *much luggage / many pieces of luggage* have you got?
b) Can you give me some *information*?
c) There *are too many* people here.
d) Let me give you *a piece of / some* advice.
e) It's difficult to find *much/any* accommodation here.
f) What *is* the news today?
g) I don't like a lot of *furniture* in a house.
h) She made some good *suggestions*.
i) I like men with long wavy *hair*.
j) Some children *are* very noisy.

Quantity

7

a) some   b) much   c) no   d) a lot of   e) a few   f) a little
g) a lot of   h) any   i) some   j) few

VOCABULARY 2

Eating and drinking

8

b) cow   c) spinach   d) plum   e) barbecue   f) toffee

Phrasal verbs

9

a, b, d, f, g and i are correct.

10

b) Hand in   c) take in   d) turn in   e) Drop in   f) come in
g) put in   h) bring in

Unit 16

READING

1

a) False   b) False   c) True   d) False   e) True   f) True

2

Positive.

4

a) Pet tarantulas breed easily.
b) They always give a warning, by rearing up.
c) Most tarantulas kept as pets come from North and South America.
d) It is better to keep tarantulas apart.
e) An aquarium is the ideal home for them.
f) Male tarantulas live for only a year.

GRAMMAR

Reporting statements and questions

5

a) … thought that British people cared more for …
b) … nobody had yet done anything …
c) … people really had to stop animals polluting …
d) … would leave their money to their pets when they died.
e) … if he would support the campaign against …

Reporting verbs

6

b) explain   c) invited   d) complained   e) advised
f) reminded

VOCABULARY

Animals

7

b) tiger   c) leopard   d) gorilla   e) zebra   f) hippopotamus
g) bear   h) kangaroo

Classifications

8

b) insects   c) birds   d) fish   e) abbreviations   f) transport
g) relations

PRONUNCIATION

Problem consonants

9

a) /ʒ/ garage, pleasure, usual, leisure
   /ʃ/ special, sugar, ocean, precious
b) /z/ news, close (*verb*), his, lose
   /s/ glass, face, list, bicycle
c) /ð/ mother, weather, that, other
   /θ/ bath, thank, fourth, birthday

WRITING

Direct speech

10

'I remember seeing a tall woman with a small dog who seemed very upset about something,' David told them.
   'What time was that?' asked the sergeant.
   'I can't remember exactly,' David replied.
   'Can you give me precise details of what you did between leaving work and arriving home?' the Inspector asked me.
   'I had a drink with my boss in the cocktail bar next to my office, and then I made a phone call before cycling home,' I replied.
   'We are going to interview everyone in the neighbourhood,' explained the sergeant. 'Will you telephone the police station if you think of anything else which might be useful?'

Unit 17

LISTENING

1

a) Bruce is terrified of deep water.
b) Sue has a phobia about wasps.
c) Jane doesn't like lifts, going underground or going below decks in ships.
d) Marie has a fear of falling into a hole / of heights.

2

a) He fell into a pond when he was two years old and nearly drowned.
b) They look aggressive and behave aggressively.
c) She can't stay still in a room if she sees a wasp.
d) Bees seem much gentler and just go about their business.
e) Because she fell on her face in the mud in a cave in Derbyshire.
f) She was dancing on the metal cover.
g) That there was a great hole underneath.

VOCABULARY 1

Fear

3

2 panicky
3 shake
4 brave
5 coward
6 nerve
7 hysterically
8 vomited
9 agony
10 courage

Adjectives and prepositions

4

b) in   c) of   d) about   e) for   f) with   g) of   h) to
i) from   j) with

GRAMMAR

The *-ing* form

5

b) Biting your *nails is a bad habit.*
c) Reading *without glasses will give you a headache.*
d) I know nothing *about using computers.*
e) No *parking here!*
f) Driving *long distances makes me tired.*
g) I think *spelling is* very difficult.
h) The *singing at La Scala* was brilliant.

-ing or *to*?

6

b) to wear   c) to see   d) taking   e) not to be   f) making
g) to be   h) worrying   i) to get   j) to kill   k) seeing
l) to dance   m) to go   n) going

VOCABULARY 2

Adjectives into verbs

7

The following adjectives can be used as verbs:
a) *tidy*, c) *calm*, d) *separate*, f) *dry*, g) *clean*, i) *equal*, j) *warm.*

8

-ify: *beautify, electrify, purify*
-ise: *dramatise, centralise, Americanise, legalise*
-en: *fatten, widen, lengthen, sweeten*

WRITING

9

Example story:
Last summer, Basil and Vanessa had their first holiday abroad.

The first problem was that the plane was delayed by eight hours and they had to sleep at the airport. It was in the middle of August, it was very hot and there were thousands of people. Basil suffers from claustrophobia. So it was not a good beginning to the holiday.

The next problem was that the plane was overbooked and Basil and Vanessa had to sit in different parts of the plane. Vanessa was in the smoking part even though she is allergic to smoke. On top of that, both of them are terrified of flying.

When they got to their holiday destination they found that the local representative for the travel agent spoke very bad English and that the hotel was dirty and miles from the beach. Vanessa is terrified of rats and one night saw a rat in the bathroom. Basil got food poisoning and was very ill.

What really made them angry, though, was that there were many extra charges which were not mentioned in the brochure. As a result they decided they would never go abroad again!

Unit 18

READING

1

a) a medium   b) psychic   c) a ghost   d) a poltergeist

2

a) 2   b) 3   c) 1   d) 4

3

a) … the poltergeist had taken it.
b) … ring the people who had sent it and ask them to cancel it and send another.
c) … no one else knew they had given him that name.
d) … had arranged the covers and put the toys at the end of the bed.
e) … she had (had) a terrible feeling.

GRAMMAR

Past Perfect or Past Simple?

4

b) had finished / finished
c) had interviewed
d) went out
e) stopped / had stopped
f) saw
g) hadn't written

Past Perfect Simple or Continuous?

5

b) I had been sitting in a traffic jam for 45 minutes, another motorist had bumped into me and I had got completely lost.
c) She had been waiting for an hour, she'd drunk six cups of tea and they still had not arrived.
d) I'd been studying every day for two months and I'd given up seeing my friends.

Sequencing events

6

Example story:
b) They had read in a newspaper that the house next door was haunted.
c) One night, after their parents had gone to bed, Jill and Nick went out.
d) They asked Steve to come with them, but he said he was too scared.
e) Shortly after they arrived they heard a strange noise, and saw a white shape in the garden.
f) They screamed, and ran away.
g) Then they heard laughing and saw that someone was chasing them down the street.
h) It was their cousin, who had dressed up in a white sheet to frighten them.

VOCABULARY

Ways of speaking

7

b) chatting   c) swear   d) whisper   e) gossip   f) groans

Say, speak, tell or *talk*?

8

b) talking   c) speak   d) saying   e) say   f) speak   g) tell

Make or *do*?

9

make: an appointment; a journey; progress; a mistake; a
   complaint
do: an exam; the dishes; business; harm

PRONUNCIATION

Diphthongs

10

B eight, /aɪ/   C though, /aʊ/   D mouse, /əʊ/

Unit 19

LISTENING

1

a) Yes   b) No   c) Yes   d) No   e) No   f) Yes   g) No
h) No   i) Yes

2

a) To pay the tuition fees.
b) She worked as a credit clerk.
c) Because it was a very large company.
d) Because her husband had lost his job.
e) That he was paid more than the women because he was
   a man.
f) That he might have a family one day.

3

a) … was at college, I worked …
b) … calls people up and ask them to please pay …
c) … we were only going to be there …
d) … had to go back to work because her husband … he
   had worked at for …
e) … she had been a housewife working at home for …
f) … they hired a middle-aged man to do the same …
g) … is this man getting paid more: 25% more?'
h) … wouldn't give us any more, not even the woman who
   was …

GRAMMAR

The passive

4

a) will be sent
b) was being questioned; should be given
c) had been bitten; Was he taken
d) have been included; are told

5

a) is now thought
b) would not be disturbed
c) have been raised
d) will be elected
e) to be given
f) was first published
g) had been stolen
h) was being repainted

VOCABULARY

Words often confused

6

a) lost *her keys.*
   failed *her music exams.*
   missed *the class.*
b) beat *him at tennis.*
   wins *at cards.*
   earn much *as a teacher.*
c) spilt *wine on his trousers.*
   dropped *the box on his foot.*
   fell *over in the mud.*

7

a) i) was born ii) birthday
b) i) raised ii) rose
c) i) remarkd ii) notice
d) i) confused ii) embarrassed
e) i) announced ii) advised

PRONUNCIATION

Contrastive stress

8

Examples:
b) 'Well, you're wrong. I *live in **India**.*'
c) 'Really! I thought *there were more **men** (students).*'
d) 'Well, one has arrived but *the **other** two haven't.*'
e) 'Last week the weather wasn't too bad but *the week
   before it was **awful** / this week it has been **awful**.*'
f) 'No, it's *an old, **blue** one.*'

Silent letters

9

a) *h* not pronounced: honest, hour, exhausted
   b not pronounced: lamb, doubt, climbing
b) *w*rong, *k*now, iron, lis*t*en, ta*l*k, dau*gh*ter
c) cu*p*board, si*g*n, recei*p*t, cha*l*k, autum*n*, plou*gh*, yac*h*t

WRITING

Similar spellings

10

a) diary   b) peace   c) priced   d) greet   e) raisins   f) pour

11

a) ensure   b) impotence   c) m*oi*st   d) l*ie*s   e) su*i*t
f) c*u*rse

Unit 20

GRAMMAR

Review of verb forms

1

1	**were flying**	11	had bought
2	announced	12	had cost
3	am going to	13	were feeling
4	were	14	escaped
5	had sold	15	have been living
6	moved	16	work
7	had been living	17	have learned
8	had been feeling	18	don't know
9	used to spend	19	will happen
10	talked	20	go

Sentence transformation

2

b) She has *been living / lived in that house since 1989*.
c) The man *(who lives) next door is really unpleasant*.
d) You *needn't / don't have to knock*.
e) If you *don't have an injection you may/might/could get cholera*.
f) There isn't *any coffee left*.
g) She *has been told the news*.
h) She wishes *(that) she lived in a hot country*.
i) Not *much progress has been made*.
j) If I *had enough money I would/could buy your car*.

Spot the errors

3

b) I *used* to speak …
c) … until they *arrive*.
d) … scared *of* tarantulas.
e) I haven't got *any* milk.
f) … *do* you?
g) … *to find* a job.
h) … very *fast*.
i) *How long* has he …
j) I'll ring *you up* later.
k) … listening *to* him …

PRONUNCIATION

Sounds

4

b) tea   c) put   d) cheer   e) most   f) eight   g) word
h) bean   i) land

VOCABULARY

Word building

5

b) beautiful   c) criminals   d) useful   e) overslept
f) rewrite   g) popularity   h) modernise   i) unreliable
j) hunger

Test your vocabulary

6

b) sister-in-law   c) chemist('s)   d) dial   e) fine
f) bungalow   g) stale   h) take after   i) insect   j) call off

WRITING

Linking expressions

7

b) I finished my meal. Then I went out.
  After I (had) finished my meal I went out.
c) While she was watching he was cooking the meal.
  She was watching TV. Meanwhile, he was cooking the meal.
d) He had a bath. Afterwards, he phoned her.
  He had a bath before he phoned her.
e) Although everyone else enjoyed the film, I found it very boring.
  Everyone else enjoyed the film. However, I found it very boring.
f) I didn't study at all so I failed my exams.
  I didn't study at all. As a result, I failed my exams.
g) Even though I wasn't hungry, I ate the meal.
  I wasn't hungry. Nevertheless, I ate the meal.

Dictation

8

A: I once *heard this story about a young medical student* who needed a skeleton for his studies. *The trouble was, he couldn't afford to buy one,* so he decided to go to a cemetery …
B: *To dig up some bones?*
A: Yes*, but as he was opening a dirty,* old coffin he could hear groaning, *and he was so terrified that he* grabbed the first thing he could see, *which was a leg bone.*
B: What happened next?
A: Well, *he ran back to his flat as fast as he could.* He rushed up the stairs *to the third floor,* where he lived, *and threw the bone under the bed.*
B: I suppose *it disappeared?*
A: No. *Later on he switched the light out and went to bed.* Then he heard *a noise downstairs.* Someone *had opened the front door and was coming up the stairs.* The noise stopped at his door, *and he could see, in the moonlight,* the handle starting to turn, and he heard this voice saying, *'Give me back my bone!'*
B: And did he?
A: Oh yes. *He shouted 'Take it!' and threw it* at whatever it was. And that's the end of the story!

PRONUNCIATION

Short and long vowels

12 [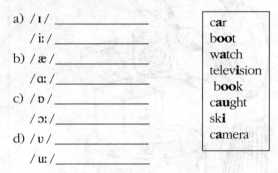 11.2] Listen to the sounds below. Then listen to the words in the box and write them in the correct gaps, according to the sounds of the letters in **bold**.

a) / ɪ / _____

/ iː / _____

b) / æ / _____

/ ɑː / _____

c) / ɒ / _____

/ ɔː / _____

d) / ʊ / _____

/ uː / _____

car
b**oo**t
w**a**tch
telev**i**sion
b**oo**k
c**au**ght
sk**i**
c**a**mera

Sound and spelling

13 The vowel letters *a, e, i, o, u* can have the following vowel sounds.

1 *a* / æ / cat
_____

2 *e* / e / let
_____

3 *i* / ɪ / sit
_____

4 *o* / ɒ / lost
_____

5 *u* / ʌ / must
_____

Other combinations of vowel letters in certain words can also have these sounds. Example: / e / – *let, head*. Write words from the box below each of the words above, according to the sound of the letters in **bold**.

c**ou**ple   v**e**st   c**ou**gh   c**u**t   b**ui**ld   r**ea**dy
tr**ou**ble   fr**o**st   **a**ction   fr**ie**nd   en**ou**gh
l**i**ft   h**ea**lth   bl**oo**d

WRITING

14 Write a dialogue between a waiter and a customer, using the cues below.

WAITER
Greet customer and ask if he/she has reserved a table.
CUSTOMER
You haven't reserved a table. Ask for a table near the window.
WAITER
Agree. Offer to take his/her coat.
CUSTOMER
Thank him/her. Ask to see the menu.
WAITER
Give the menu. Ask if he/she wants a drink.
CUSTOMER
Order a drink. Ask for ashtray.
WAITER
Apologise. Say the restaurant is no smoking only. Ask for his/her order.
CUSTOMER
Order a meal.

_____

_____

_____

_____

_____

_____

_____

_____

_____

_____

_____

_____

_____

_____

_____

_____

Money, money, money

READING

1 Look at the title and introduction to the article.

2 Read the article and make a note, on a separate sheet of paper, of:

a) the 'tricks' which help manufacturers sell their products.

b) how the customer 'foots the bill'.

3 Give an example of what colour, according to the text, you think the packets of the following are likely to be.

a) face creams _____

b) bran _____

c) ice cream _____

d) expensive chocolates _____

_____

e) painkillers _____

4 Write *T* (for *True*) and *F* (for *False*) next to the statements below.

a) Manufacturers will persuade us of something that is not true, if necessary, in order to sell their products. _____

b) The colouring of the packaging depends on which manufacturer produces it. _____

c) Shoppers don't always get the same amount as they think they are buying. _____

d) All manufacturers spend a lot on packaging. _____

e) Cosmetics companies often spend more than half the cost of their product on presentation. _____

It costs a pretty packet!

Manufacturers have all sorts of tricks to make us buy their products but in the end it's the customer who foots the bill.

1 Shopping is not as simple as you may think! There are all sorts of psychological and eye-deceiving tricks at play each time we reach out for that particular brand of product on the shelf.

2 Colouring, for example, varies according to what the manufacturers are trying to sell. Most cosmetics are packaged in delicate pastel colours such as pink. Health foods come in greens, yellows or browns because we think of these as healthy colours. Ice cream packets are often blue because we identify that as a cool colour; and luxury goods, like expensive chocolates, are invariably gold or silver.

3 When a brand of pain killer was brought out recently, researchers found that pastel colours turned the customer off because they made the product look weak and ineffective. Eventually, it came on the market in a dark blue and white package – blue because we associate it with safety, and white for calmness.

4 The size of a product can attract a shopper. But quite often a jar or bottle doesn't contain as much as it appears to. Recently a cosmetics company was successfully prosecuted for marketing a jar of make-up which gave the impression it contained far more than it actually did.

5 All the research behind the wording and presentation of packaging is obviously expensive, and there are no prizes for guessing that it is the customer who foots the bill. However, there are signs of revolution against fancy packaging: The Body Shop, for instance, sells its products in containers with handwritten labels. These bottles are practical as well as cost-effective and can be used again.

6 It is estimated that the more established cosmetics companies spend, on average, 70 per cent of the total cost of the product itself on packaging!

7 The most successful manufacturers know that it's not enough to have a good product. The founder of Pears soap, who for 25 years have used enchanting little girls to promote their goods, summed it up. 'Any fool can make soap, but it takes a genius to sell it,' he said.

(from *Bella*)

5 Look up the words *reach* (paragraph 1), *turn off* (paragraph 3) and *fancy* (paragraph 5) in a monolingual dictionary and find out which of the meanings shown best correspond to the meaning in the text. Then use one of the meanings shown in the dictionary to complete the following sentences.

a) She really _____*fancied*_____ the man she met at the party, but was too shy to speak to him.

b) We _____ the motorway at Junction 31 in order to go into Birmingham.

c) You must be very tall – your head almost _____ the ceiling.

d) When the programme finished I _____ the television.

e) Those chocolates are a bit _____ for her, aren't they? I think she'd prefer plain ones.

f) We should _____ London soon.

GRAMMAR

The second conditional

6 Make sentences expressing an imaginary situation, using the sentences as cues.

a) Animals can't speak. They can't tell us when they are unhappy.
   If animals could speak they would be able to tell us when they were unhappy.

b) Unfortunately I don't live in New York. I can't afford it.

_____

_____

c) You are not a good musician. You don't practise enough.

_____

_____

d) I am not young so I won't change my job.

_____

_____

e) I haven't got any time, so I can't help her.

_____

_____

f) You don't have a teaching qualification. You can't work here.

_____

_____

Conditionals and *wish*

7 Continue or make responses to the following sentences, using the prompts in brackets. Conditional sentences may be possible or imaginary.

a) I've got a bad stomachache. (*Give advice*: If / take / this medicine / feel better)
   If you take this medicine you'll feel better.

b) My car's broken down again. (*Express regret*: wish / new one)

_____

_____

c) This job doesn't pay enough. (*Give advice*: If / I / you / get another job)

_____

_____

_____

d) I am having problems selling my house. (*Express regret*: wish / sell / my house)

_____

_____

_____

e) I almost had an accident. (*Give a warning*: Unless / stop drinking and driving / kill yourself)

_____

_____

_____

f) I haven't enough time to come to the party. (*Express regret*: wish / time / come)

_____

_____

_____

Prepositional phrases

8 On a separate sheet of paper combine the prepositions in the first box with the nouns in the second box to make prepositional phrases. Example: *on the left*

in on by at	the left car business television work accident trouble hospital time university fire foot the telephone mistake love pencil home road the cinema

VOCABULARY

Buying

9   Fill the gaps below with words from the box.

> credit card   bargain   receipt   refund
> discount   half-price

a) This coat is incredibly cheap. It's a real _____.

b) Ask the assistant to give you a _____ in case you have to bring it back.

c) The computer he bought didn't work properly so the shop gave him a _____.

d) I haven't got much cash. Do you think they'll accept a _____?

e) The staff at our shop get 10% _____ on everything they buy.

f) This cheese is _____. It's probably because today is the 'sell by' date.

PRONUNCIATION

Vowel sounds

10   Put the words in the box in the correct column, depending on the vowel sounds. Then use your dictionary to check if you were right.

> friend   lose   law   could   food   match   field
> put   rich   hand   son   third   watch   heart
> build   cough   blood   key   ought   can't
> word   says

/ iː /	/ e /	/ uː /
seen	_pen_	_true_
_____	_____	_____
_____	_____	_____

/ ɪ /	/ ɒ /	/ ɜː /
bin	_lot_	_girl_
_____	_____	_____
_____	_____	_____

/ æ /	/ ʌ /	/ ʊ /
cat	_cup_	_book_
_____	_____	_____
_____	_____	_____

/ ɑː /	/ ɔː /
dark	_short_
_____	_____
_____	_____

WRITING

Dictation

11   [🔊 12.1]   Listen to the recording and write down what B says. Write down numbers, rather than words, when they are used.

a) A: Excuse me. How much are these oranges?

   B: _____

   _____

b) A: Those grapes look lovely.

   B: _____

   _____

c) A: Let's park here, shall we?

   B: _____

   _____

d) A: How would you like to pay, sir?

   B: _____

   _____

e) A: Get me a bar of chocolate, will you?

   B: _____

   _____

f) A: Is it too far to drive?

   B: _____

   _____

g) A: How many miles has your car done?

   B: _____

Layabout

LISTENING

1 [🔲 13.1]   Listen to the three speakers talking about their dreams. Circle the words in the box that are mentioned.

> flying sleeping menacing nightmare
> classroom unhappy tired naked father
> rocks illness smoking alive

2   Listen to each speaker again and write i) or ii) after each of the sentences below.

Bonnie's dream

a) She flies i) *higher than the treetops*

  ii) *as high as the treetops.* __ii__

b) The people chasing her i) *never catch her*

  ii) *always catch her.* _____

c) The dreams are i) *sometimes threatening*

  ii) *always threatening.* _____

d) They show i) *she feels insecure*

  ii) *she is sad.* _____

Ben's dream

a) His dream is i) *similar to* ii) *different from* that of other teachers. _____

b) He doesn't know i) *where he is*

  ii) *why he's there.* _____

c) He is worried about i) *not being paid*

  ii) *not being prepared.* _____

Keith's dream

a) The first dream was i) *last week*

  ii) *soon after the death.* _____

b) In the dream, his mother seemed i) *well*

  ii) *ill.* _____

c) He i) *liked* ii) *didn't like* the dreams. _____

3   Tick the sentences you think are correct. Then listen again and check your answers.

Bonnie

a) I've had a recurring dream since I was a child.

  _____

b) I've been having a recurring dream since I was a child. _____

Ben

a) I've not prepared anything. _____

b) I've not been preparing anything. _____

Keith

a) I've had incredibly vivid dreams. _____

b) I had incredibly vivid dreams. _____

GRAMMAR

Since or for?

4   Write *since* or *for* in the gaps.

a) I haven't had a cigar _____ last Christmas.

b) Maria hasn't been here _____ ages.

c) I've been trying to see you _____ two weeks.

d) Stephen has been living in Beijing _____ he left university.

e) It's been foggy _____ Tuesday.

f) I haven't been happy about our relationship _____ a long time.

How long...?

5   Write a question with *How long...?* Choose the Present Perfect Simple or the Present Perfect Continuous. In some cases, both are possible.

a) Felicity / have the flu
   How long has Felicity had the flu?

b) Stuart / teach English
   _____

   _____

c) Di / be married to Charles
   _____

   _____

d) you and Dick / look for somewhere else to live
   _____

   _____

e) you / sit on the stairs
   _____

   _____

f) she / have that job with the BBC
   _____

   _____

Present Perfect Simple or Continuous?

6   Write a sentence with *for* or *since*, using the Present Perfect Simple or the Present Perfect Continuous. In many cases you will need to change the verb.

a) I became a member of this club in 1989. It's now 1992.
   I've been a member of this club since 1989 (for three years).

b) We moved to Nigeria ten years ago.
   _____

   _____

c) The children turned on the TV at 6 p.m. It's 9 p.m. now.
   _____

   _____

d) Francis bought that bicycle last year.
   _____

   _____

e) Joanne started her homework when she got home. She's still doing it and it's bedtime.
   _____

   _____

f) She had a holiday two years ago. That was the last time she had a holiday.
   _____

   _____

Present or Present Perfect?

7 Two friends are having an argument. Put the verbs into one of the following tenses: Present Simple or Continuous, Present Perfect Simple or Continuous.

A: Go away! I (1 *not want*)_____ to talk to you.

Where (2 *you be*)_____?

B: I'm sorry. I (3 *work*)_____ late.

A: I (4 *not believe*)_____ you.

B: What do you think I (5 *do*)_____? What

(6 *you suggest*)_____?

A: Why (7 *you come*)_____ now at this time

of night? It's too late. I (8 *wait*)_____

_____ for you for more than three hours. I

(9 *not eat*)_____ a thing and I'm tired.

B: Why (10 *you shout*)_____ at me?

A: Why (11 *you think*)_____? I (12 *have*)

_____ enough of you. I

(13 *never want*)_____ to see you again.

VOCABULARY

Idiomatic expressions: pairs

8 Fill in the gaps by choosing one of the following expressions.

| here and there   rightly or wrongly   short and sweet |
| one or two   hard and fast   free and easy   there and then |
| more and more |

a) I've invited _____ friends round

this evening. I hope you can come.

b) Graham thinks, _____, that he has been

badly treated.

c) You lead a _____ life, don't you?

Nothing seems to worry you.

d) It's dreadful! Clothes are getting _____

expensive.

e) He proposed to her and she accepted _____

_____.

f) You're not that young! In fact, I can see a grey hair _____

_____

g) There are no _____ rules. You can

do what you like.

h) Make your talk _____! Don't let the

audience get bored.

WRITING

Summary writing

9   Read the article opposite. Then complete the following sentences on a separate sheet of paper in order to summarise each paragraph.

Paragraph 1: Different people _____

_____

_____

Paragraph 2: Energetic people _____

_____

_____

Paragraph 3: There's no point in trying to sleep

more _____

_____

_____

Paragraph 4: It's better to learn to relax _____

_____

_____

Paragraph 5: Lack of sleep _____

_____

_____

Paragraph 6: The reason we can't always get to

sleep _____

_____

Paragraph 7: If we are angry or stressed _____

_____

_____

10   On a separate sheet of paper, write a summary of the article, in no more than 100 words, beginning: *The important thing about sleep...* Use your own words as far as possible.

Wouldn't it be lovely to get a good night's sleep!
by Doctor Johnson

1   Eight hours sleep is traditionally regarded as healthy – though many of us need less, and some more. What matters is how you feel, and what you do with the other sixteen hours of the day.

2   We are all built slightly differently, so there is no reason why our sleep requirements should be the same. If, for example, you are the sort of person who goes running around getting exhausted, then you are going to need more rest, but not necessarily more sleep.

3   Similarly, if you sleep 'badly', wake tense, and worry throughout the day – and there's nothing more tiring than tension – then further long hours lying awake won't help.

4   Drugged sleep is not the long-term answer either. Sleeping pills merely slow your body down. Usually they let you drop off, though if you take them for more than six weeks, then the actual chemical effect disappears. The only real solution is 'turning off' the internal machinery. Work at creating your own relaxing routine, get hold of the things that annoy you most and try to identify them.

5   What is sleep all about? The simplest way to find out what sleep is for is to do without it for a while and see what happens. The brain starts going gently crazy if deprived of sleep for two or three days. It simply stops working in a sensible fashion.

6   Why does sleep sometimes not come when it should? Imagine the days when our ancestors lived in the jungle. Those who fell asleep too easily risked being eaten up. It certainly paid to keep half-awake, ready for action if danger arrived. The trouble is we are still doing it even though there is no longer any danger. We react as if there are threats to our existence, when all we want to do is fall asleep.

7   Anger and other signs of stress clearly interfere with calm sleep, just as they do with calm waking. Before trying to sleep, it is always better to get your angry feelings out into the open, rather than push them to the back of your mind. As you fall asleep, the mind is less lively and allows those feelings to come back again, where they dance around and keep you awake.

8   I recommend trying to get more control of reality. Then your dreams will be sweeter and your sleep more refreshing.

(from PLUS)

Leisure

Tony Lamb

READING

1 The information below is about someone's hobby but the sentences are in the wrong order. Number each sentence (1–7) to indicate the correct order. Look carefully for linking words (e.g. *and*) which will help you.

a) This is quite difficult at times, as I have a really bad memory. _____

b) There are loads of rehearsals, as well, which take up nearly all my spare time. _____

c) It's something I had never thought of doing, but then I saw an advert in the local newspaper, saying that they needed extras for a crowd scene, in a film they were making in my town. ___1___

d) In fact, if I were younger I would even think of turning professional! _____

e) I found I really enjoyed the experience, so afterwards I went for an audition at my local dramatic society. _____

f) However, it also has its really good points – you have a lot of fun preparing for and putting on the productions, and I've met so many people and made friends from different walks of life. _____

g) At first they just gave me walk-on parts, but now I sometimes play the lead, which involves an awful lot of lines to learn. _____

2 What is the hobby referred to above? _____

3 Look at the information again and underline words that are associated with this hobby. Write down any other words you know which might be connected to the hobby.

_____

_____

4 Look at the information again and answer the following questions.

a) What experience did the writer enjoy?

_____

b) What did he join as a result?

_____

c) What do you think *walk-on parts* are?

_____

d) When does he have a lot of lines to learn?

_____

e) What is *quite difficult at times*?

_____

f) Is he going to turn professional? Give reasons.

_____

VOCABULARY

Synonyms

5 The following sentences all come from the *Reading* text. Match each of the words in italics to a near synonym from the box.

pleasure free hard club

a) … which take up nearly all my *spare* time. _____

b) … at my local dramatic *society*. _____

c) This is quite *difficult* at times … _____

d) … you have a lot of *fun*. _____

Groups of words

6 In each of the following groups of words there is one word which doesn't fit. Underline the odd word out. Then give a general name to each of the groups.

A	B	C	D
<u>BOOKS</u> ___	_____	_____	_____
author	choir	soap opera	casserole
novel	conductor	documentary	spade
biography	cast	serial	weeds
<u>screen</u>	concert	channel	lawn mower
library	composer	overture	shrub

7 Put the words from A and B above on to the networks below.

a) Then add two more items to each category.

b) On a separate sheet of paper draw and fill in networks for the other vocabulary groupings C and D above.

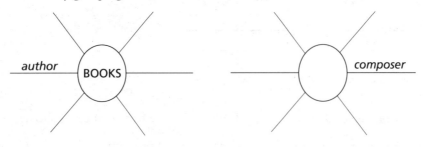

Words often confused

8 Underline the correct alternative.

a) I have *a possibility* / <u>*an opportunity*</u> to go abroad next month.

b) I am going on a *travel/trip* after my course finishes.

c) This dress doesn't *suit/fit* me. It makes me look pale.

d) If you don't hurry you'll *lose/miss* the bus.

e) I've *dropped/spilt* some wine on my new dress.

f) Why don't you come to the disco with us? It's *fun/funny*.

GRAMMAR

Necessary or not necessary?

9 Make sentences using *must, mustn't, should, (not) have to* and *needn't* based on the situations below. In some case there is more than one possibility.

a) It's Simon's first day in a new job. It's late and he's still in bed. What does his mother say to him?

'You must get up or you'll be late! You mustn't be late on your first day!'

b) Susan really hates getting up early and today is Sunday. Why is she happy?

_____

_____

c) The restaurant you went to last night was fantastic. Recommend it to your friends.

_____

_____

d) Tell your visitor not to drink the water from the tap. It's not safe.

_____

_____

e) Your son doesn't want to take the medicine the doctor recommended. You are insistent.

_____

_____

f) You are going to a dinner party. Ask someone if it's necessary to take a present for the hostess.

_____

_____

Permission and prohibition

10 Rewrite the signs below, using one of the following expressions: *are/aren't allowed, can/can't, mustn't*. Sometimes more than one answer is possible.

a) You are _____ *not allowed* _____ to smoke in the toilets.

NO SMOKING IN THE TOILETS

b) Customers _____ use their credit cards.

Credit cards accepted

c) You _____ to visit before 5 p.m.

Visiting hours from 5 - 9 p.m.

d) You _____ go in unless you are a member.

Members only

e) You _____ take any photographs.

PHOTOGRAPHY IS FORBIDDEN

f) You _____ to stay up to two hours.

Parking restricted to 2 hours

Obligation, prohibition, permission (past)

11 A daughter (*D*) is asking her mother (*M*) about her life when she was young. Use expressions of obligation, prohibition and permission in the past to complete the dialogue below.

D: When you were young (1 *wear*)_*were you*_
_*allowed to wear*___ make-up?

M: No, certainly not. Not until I was about 20. And
I (2 *wear*)_____
the clothes that my mother bought me.

D: How awful! And (3 *stay*)_____
_____ at school until you were 16?

M: No, it wasn't illegal to leave before 16, as it is
now. In fact most children (4 *leave*)_____
_____ school at 14 because their
parents wanted them to earn money.

D: (5 *go out*)_____
_____ with boys when you were my age?

M: Only if a grown-up was with you. You (6 *go*)
_____,
out alone to discos as you do now, oh no!

PRONUNCIATION

Weak forms

Many grammatical words are pronounced weakly and so are said more quickly than the stressed, content words in a sentence. Example:
*He **can** (/kən/) rehearse **at** (/ət/) weekends.*

12 [▦ 14.1] In each of the following short dialogues one of the two words in italics is pronounced weakly. Listen to the recording and underline the weak forms.

a) A: I *can* speak Spanish quite well now.

   B: *Can* you? That's very good!

b) A: I think they *were* at the cinema last night.

   B: No, I'm sure they *weren't*.

c) A: You turn right *at* the post office.

   B: *At* the post office or after it?

d) A: I've got a present *for* Tim.

   B: Did you say *for* him or from him?

e) A: You *must* remember his birthday this year!

   B: Yes, I *must* buy him a really nice present.

WRITING

Punctuation and layout

13 On a separate sheet of paper rewrite this letter, punctuating it and laying it out correctly.

> 63 east st hastings
> cb2 4xj
> 11th february 1991
> dear aunt pat i am writing to thank you for the lovely present you sent me it arrived on thursday and ive been wearing it all week its lovely and warm so i really appreciate it very much isnt the weather horrible and cold at the moment im sorry that i cant get down to see you this weekend but if i can id like to come another weekend eg the last weekend in this month anyway write and tell me if thats all right and ill see you soon lots of love mark ps have you heard from janice recently

Abbreviations

14 The following abbreviations are often used in letters. Match the abbreviations to their definitions.

a) etc.	1	that is to say
b) i.e.	2	as soon as possible
c) RSVP	3	répondez, s'il vous plaît (please
d) PS		reply)
e) e.g.	4	please turn over (the page)
f) c.f.	5	for example
g) PTO	6	et cetera (and so on)
h) a.s.a.p.	7	compare
	8	postscript (a note at the end of
		a letter)

A meal or murder?

VOCABULARY 1

Food

1 In the spaces, write the names of the various kinds of food in the pictures using expressions in the box below.

| can   box   bag   half a kilo   packet   jar |
| bottle   pot   half a dozen   loaf   tin   piece |
| leg   bar |

1   *a packet of spaghetti*

2 _____

3 _____   4 _____   5 _____

6 _____   7 _____   8 _____

9 _____   10 _____   11 _____

12 _____   13 _____   14 _____

LISTENING

2 [☐ 15.1]   Listen to Ed talking about what he eats and drinks. On a separate sheet of paper, copy the following column headings: *some, quite a lot, a lot, not much/many, almost none.* Under the different headings write down how much Ed eats and drinks of each kind of food.

53

3 Listen again and complete the sentences.

a) Ed and his wife don't eat Indian food at home because _____

_____

b) The reason Ed tries to cut down on beef is that

_____

_____

c) He _____

since it's rather expensive.

d) He now drinks herbal teas. However, _____

_____

e) Although he doesn't eat many salads in winter

_____

f) The sugar in soft drinks _____

_____

g) Ed would lose weight if _____

_____

h) He thinks additives are not good for him so ___

_____

_____

4 Try to fill in the gaps in the following extracts from the recording. Then listen again and check your answers.

a) ... as to the type of food I eat, I don't _____

_____ meat.

b) ... broccoli especially – that's _____

_____ ones – courgettes ...

c) ... try to _____

fruit every day ...

d) I _____ if ever drink soft drinks ...

GRAMMAR

Countable or uncountable?

5 Tick which of the following are uncountable. (In most dictionaries uncountable nouns are marked *U* and countable nouns *C*.)

a) box   _____   e) smoke   _____

b) water   ✔   f) house   _____

c) education _____   g) bread   _____

d) knee   _____   h) money   _____

6 Correct these sentences.

a) How many luggages have you got?

_____

_____

b) Can you give me some informations?

_____

_____

c) There is too much people here.

_____

d) Let me give you an advice.

_____

_____

e) It's difficult to find many accommodation here.

_____

_____

f) What are the news today?

_____

_____

g) I don't like a lot of furnitures in a house.

_____

_____

h) She made some good suggestion.

_____

_____

i) I like men with long wavy hairs.

_____

_____

j) Some children is very noisy.

_____

_____

Quantity

7 Underline the correct alternative.

a) Could I have *some/any* more soup?

b) They haven't got *much/some/many* money in the bank.

c) There's *many / a few / no* milk in the fridge.

d) Sorry, but there's not *many / a lot of / some* time to talk.

e) I've saved you *a little / a few / any / much* sweets.

f) Would you like *a little / a few* orange juice?

g) What *much / many / a lot of* flowers!

h) You never give me *some/any* help!

i) I think we need *some/any* more jam.

j) Sadly, there are *a few / few / not much* flowers in the garden now.

VOCABULARY 2

Eating and drinking

8 Put a circle round the odd one in each of these. Use your dictionary if necessary.

a) cod, haddock, (pheasant,) salmon, trout

b) lamb, pork, bacon, cow, veal

c) spinach, date, pineapple, peach, cherry

d) cabbage, pea, cucumber, carrot, plum

e) lunch, dinner, supper, barbecue, breakfast

f) squash, toffee, mineral water, cocoa, lager

Phrasal verbs

9 Read the following examples carefully.

He looked the word up in the dictionary. ✔
He looked up the word in the dictionary. ✔

He looked it up. ✔
He looked up it. ✗

Put a tick next to the correct sentences.

a) Please give it back. _____

b) My boss told me off. _____

c) I'll ring up you later. _____

d) Look after this, will you? _____

e) If you do that again, I'll kick out you. _____

f) Put that gun down! _____

g) Put down that gun! _____

h) Put down it. _____

i) Put it down. _____

10 Rewrite the sentences below, replacing the expressions in italics with phrasal verbs made from the verbs in the box plus *in* (e.g. *turn in*). Use a dictionary if necessary.

turn bring drop put take come hand check

a) **What time do we have to *report our arrival*?**

   What time do we have to check in?

b) *Give* your homework to me at the end of the class.

   _____

c) It took me ages to *understand fully* what she was saying.

   _____

d) After midnight most people decided to *go to bed*.

   _____

e) *Come and see me at home* if you have time.

   _____

f) When did short skirts first *become fashionable*?

   _____

g) Why don't you *make an application* for that job?

   _____

h) The Government should *introduce* new laws to protect animals.

   _____

WRITING

11 Look at these three pictures and headlines used in campaigns against cruelty to animals. On a separate sheet of paper write an advertisement to support *one* of these campaigns.

Does your mother have a fur coat? – His mother lost hers.

So you love animals? – For school dinner?

The cruel circus. – Have you come to laugh at the misery of animals?

Beastly tales

READING

1 How much do you know about tarantulas? Using your general knowledge, write *T* (for *True*) or *F* (for *False*) next to each of the following.

a) The name *tarantula* means 'spider'. _____

b) Tarantulas are dangerous if they bite. _____

c) There are about 300 different kinds of tarantulas. _____

d) The average tarantula is 20 cm (10") across. _____

e) Bird spiders live in trees. _____

f) They change their skins every year. _____

2 Guess what the headline means. Use a dictionary to help you. Then decide whether you think the article will be positive or negative towards tarantulas.

3 Read the text and check your answers to Exercise 1, correcting them as necessary.

4 Correct the following statements.

a) Pet tarantulas don't usually have babies.

_____

b) They attack without warning.

_____

c) Most tarantulas kept as pets come from Africa.

_____

d) It is better to keep tarantulas together.

_____

e) A cardboard box is the ideal home for them.

_____

f) Male tarantulas live for a long time.

_____
_____

TARANTULA: CRAWLY, BUT NOT CREEPY

Although they are not everybody's idea of the perfect pet, tarantulas are fascinating to look after, breed quite easily and are becoming increasingly popular. Their reputedly deadly bites are, in fact, no worse than bee stings; they only attack when provoked, and always give prior warning by rearing up.

The name tarantula dates back to the Middle Ages when it referred to spiders living in the Italian town of Tarantum, whose bites were thought to cause a fever, 'tarantism'. As Europeans travelled into tropical areas they found much larger spiders which also became known as tarantulas and now there are about 300 varieties in the tarantula family. They range in breadth from an average 7.5 cm (3") to the huge tree-inhabiting bird spiders which can have a leg span of 25 cm (10") and weigh 85 g (3 oz). North and South American tarantulas are most often kept as pets. One of the most popular and colourful is the Mexican red-leg.

WHAT YOU NEED TO KNOW

- **Housing** Keep tarantulas apart as they may fight. A covered aquarium (to prevent any climbing out) with a wood-based floor is ideal. Provide something for them to hide under, and branches for bird spiders. The temperature should be about 29˚C (85˚F).
- **Feeding** Small insects, such as live crickets, should be offered several times a week. Always provide water.
- **Health** Never smoke near your tarantula, as nicotine will kill it. Adult spiders moult yearly and emerge from their old skin within a day.
- **Lifespan** Males (which have a claw on each of their first legs) may live for only a year but females can live for 10 years.
- **Cost** From about £20.

(from *Best*)

GRAMMAR

Reporting statements and questions

5   On a recent 'chat' programme on television with a panel of animal lovers the interviewer said the following things. Report her questions and comments.

a) 'Do you think that British people care more for their pets than for their children?'
She asked if they _____
_____

b) 'Nobody has yet done anything to stop cruelty in circuses.'
She commented that _____
_____

c) 'People really must stop animals polluting our streets.'
She said that _____
_____

d) 'Will you leave your money to your pets when you die?'
She asked if they _____
_____

e) 'Will you support the campaign against fur coats?'
She asked a young man _____
_____

Reporting verbs

6   Use a word from the box in the correct form in order to fill in the gaps. Check the meaning of the verbs in a dictionary if necessary.

advise   invite   complain   explain   remind warn

a) I hope somebody has ___*warned*___ you that fireworks can be dangerous.
b) Can you _____ what this means?
c) They've _____ us to stay for the weekend.
d) They _____ to the waiter about the bill.
e) She had such terrible toothache that he _____ her to go to the dentist at once.
f) I _____ him of the date and he rang his father up to wish him a happy birthday.

VOCABULARY

Animals

7   Re-order the letters to spell the names of the animals in the pictures.

a) fiegrfa   ____*giraffe*____
b) greti   _____
c) pedlroa   _____
d) logalri   _____
e) beazr   _____
f) pmioshpauotp   _____
g) arbe   _____
h) aarnokgo   _____

Classifications

8 Complete the gaps to find the classifications for each group of words.

a) ring, necklace, bracelet, brooch _je w e l l e r y_

b) bee, wasp, beetle, fly __ __ s __ c __ __ __

c) sparrow, pigeon, robin, swallow __ i __ d __

d) cod, sole, shark, sardine __ __ s __

e) MP, BBC, USA, PTO

　　 a __ __ r __ __ i __ __ i __ __ s

f) bicycle, train, helicopter, ship

　　 __ r __ n __ __ o __ t

g) mother, aunt, grandfather, nephew

　　 r __ __ __ t __ __ n __

PRONUNCIATION

Problem consonants

9 Divide the words in each box according to the consonant sounds of the letters in **bold**.

a)

ga**r**a**g**e spe**c**ial **s**ugar plea**s**ure u**s**ual ocean pre**c**ious lei**s**ure

/ʒ/	/ʃ/
garage	

b)

gla**ss** new**s** clo**s**e (*verb*) fa**c**e li**s**t hi**s** lo**s**e bi**c**ycle

/z/	/s/
	glass

c)

mo**th**er ba**th** wea**th**er **th**ank **th**at four**th** o**th**er bir**th**day

/ð/	/θ/
mother	

WRITING

Direct speech

10 Read the summary of a conversation between two policemen and two men (David and Jim). Rewrite it in direct speech, on a separate sheet of paper, remembering to include punctuation features of dialogues, such as speech marks. Begin like this: *'Did you see anybody strange in the area last night?' the police asked us.*

"The police asked us if we'd seen anybody strange in the area the previous night. David told them he remembered seeing a tall woman with a small dog who had seemed very upset about something. The sergeant asked him what time that had been but David couldn't remember exactly.

Then the Inspector asked me to give precise details of what I had done between leaving work and arriving home. I replied that I had had a drink with my boss in the cocktail bar next to my office and then I had made a phone call before cycling home.

The sergeant explained that they were going to interview everyone in the neighbourhood. He asked us if we would telephone the police station if we thought of anything else which might be useful."

What are you afraid of?

LISTENING

1 [📼 17.1]   Listen to the speakers below and write a sentence saying what each person is frightened of using the word in *italics*.

a) Bruce – *terrified*

_____

_____

b) Sue – *phobia*

_____

_____

c) Jane – *like*

_____

_____

d) Marie – *fear*

_____

_____

_____

2   Answer these questions.

a) What was the cause of Bruce's fear?

_____

_____

b) Why doesn't Sue like wasps?

_____

_____

c) What effect do wasps have on her?

_____

_____

d) Why doesn't she have a fear of bees?

_____

_____

e) Why did Jane have to walk around dripping in mud?

_____

_____

f) What was Marie doing on a well?

_____

_____

g) What didn't she realise?

_____

_____

VOCABULARY 1

Fear

3   Read the following text and complete the gaps using a word from the box.

coward   courage   shake   vomited   anxiety
agony   panicky   brave   hysterically   nerve

DENTAL TERROR

Half the population are letting their teeth rot rather than go to the dentist.

Paul O'Neill, 38, finally overcame his (1) *anxiety* through hypnosis. 'I was so (2)_____ I used to (3)_____ the night before my appointment and be completely unable to sleep. It all started when I was a child and the surgery looked like a torture chamber to me with all those heavy wires, drills and the gas mask. They quickly turned a (4)_____ child into a (5)_____.

'Then to top it all, my dentist took out a (6)_____ and showed it to me. It looked like a thin, white maggot, and when I saw it, I screamed (7)_____ and (8)_____ right there in the chair.

'After that I didn't go back for years – it's a wonder I've got any teeth left. But I had to go when I was in (9)_____. These days I have hypnosis, my (10)_____ has returned and I actually enjoy going to the dentist.'

(from *Chat*)

Adjectives and prepositions

4 Underline the correct alternatives.

a) I'm not very good *in/at/about* French.

b) Are you interested *in/at/of* Sumo wrestling?

c) Mike says he's scared *about/of/by* snakes.

d) She's very glad *about/in/with* her new job.

e) I feel very sorry *about/of/for* her with a boyfriend like that!

f) He got promotion because he was friendly *for/ with/of* the manager.

g) Robert's very jealous *about/of/by* other men.

h) Don't be so rude *to/at/of* your mother!

i) Victoria is very different *of/at/from* her sister.

j) Are you pleased *of/with/by* your new computer?

GRAMMAR

The *-ing* form

5 Rewrite the following sentences combining pairs of sentences where possible.

a) I like comedy on television. It cheers me up.
   Watching *comedy on television cheers me up.*

b) I bite my nails. It's a bad habit.
   Biting your _____

c) If you read without glasses, it'll give you a headache.
   Reading _____
   _____

d) Me use computers? I know nothing about them.
   I know nothing _____
   _____

e) You can't park here!
   No _____

f) I don't like driving long distances. It makes me tired.
   Driving _____
   _____

g) I can't spell. It's very difficult.
   I think _____
   very difficult.

h) I went to La Scala. They sang brilliantly.
   The _____
   was brilliant.

-ing or *to*?

6 Put the verbs into the correct form, using *-ing* or *to*.

a) I don't much enjoy (*go*)_____*going*_____ to horror movies.

b) Simon decided (*wear*)_____ his red socks to work.

c) I want (*see*)_____ you.

d) My sister suggested (*take*)_____ the car.

e) Will you promise (*not, be*)_____ late?

f) Would you mind (*make*)_____ less noise?

g) I expect (*be*)_____ in London tomorrow.

h) Anna gave up (*worry*)_____. If he didn't care, why should she?

i) She's hoping (*get*)_____ a better job.

j) The terrorists threatened (*kill*)_____ the hostage.

k) I don't want to miss (*see*)_____ that documentary on TV tonight.

l) Where did you learn (*dance*)_____ like that?

m) I'd love (*go*)_____ to Japan next year.

n) Let's put off (*go*)_____ out until after dinner.

VOCABULARY 2

Adjectives into verbs

7 Tick the adjectives which can also be used as verbs without any change to their written form. For example *cool* can be an adjective (*a cool evening*) or a verb (*Let your tea cool a little before you drink it.*).

a) tidy _____

b) dangerous _____

c) calm _____

d) separate _____

e) hungry _____

f) dry _____

g) clean _____

h) clever _____

i) equal _____

j) warm _____

8 Make verbs from the adjectives in the box and put them in the correct column below.

| simple   modern   strong   fat   beautiful |
| dramatic   wide   central   electric   long |
| American   pure   sweet   legal |

– ify	– ise	– en
simplify	*modernise*	*strengthen*
_____	_____	_____
_____	_____	_____
_____	_____	_____
_____	_____	_____

WRITING

9 Write a story based on the following notes. Each section (1-5) represents a paragraph but you may make as many sentences as you like in each paragraph. Change the tenses of the verbs as appropriate and add any other words you think are necessary (e.g. linking words).

1 Last summer / Basil and Vanessa / first holiday abroad.

2 First problem / plane delayed eight hours / sleep at airport. Middle of August / very hot / thousands of people. Basil suffers / claustrophobia. Not / good beginning to the holiday.

3 Plane overbooked / Basil and Vanessa / different parts of plane. Vanessa in smoking part / even though allergic to smoke. Both of them / terrified / flying.

4 Get to holiday destination / local representative for travel agent / very bad English / hotel dirty / miles from beach. Vanessa terrified of rats / one night sees rat in bathroom. Basil gets food poisoning / very ill.

5 Really angry / extra charges / not mentioned in brochure. Decide never / go abroad again.

_____

_____

_____

_____

_____

_____

_____

_____

_____

_____

_____

_____

_____

_____

_____

_____

_____

_____

_____

_____

_____

Tales of the unexpected

READING

1 Match the words in the box with their dictionary definitions.

a ghost   a poltergeist   a medium   psychic

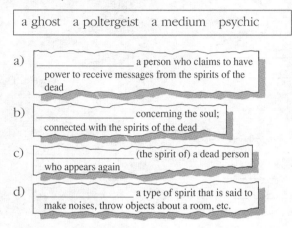

a) _____ a person who claims to have power to receive messages from the spirits of the dead

b) _____ concerning the soul; connected with the spirits of the dead

c) _____ (the spirit of) a dead person who appears again

d) _____ a type of spirit that is said to make noises, throw objects about a room, etc.

2 Read the four articles by people who have experienced something supernatural. Match the articles to the following descriptions.

a) A message from a dead baby to his mother.
_____

b) A poltergeist who likes children. _____

c) A problem with a supernatural thief. _____

d) A lucky escape because someone followed their instincts. _____

3 Complete the following sentences based on the texts.

a) Barbara couldn't find her cheque because
_____

b) After the cheque disappeared she had to
_____
_____

c) Carol burst into tears when the healer talked about Simon because _____
_____

d) When the parents went in to see their youngest child they found that a poltergeist _____
_____

1 Animal trainer, Barbara Woodhouse

'A poltergeist shares our house and the horrid thing is always stealing. Last week it took a cheque for £1,600 that I'd left on my desk and I had to ring the people who'd sent it and say, "I'm afraid the poltergeist has taken your cheque. Please cancel it and send another."

'Later that same morning he took the wedding ring right off my hand. It's awful. People don't believe me until they come here and have something stolen themselves.'

2 Actress, Carol Hawkins

'The most amazing thing happened after I lost my baby three years ago. I was being treated by a healer – a complete stranger – who said, 'I don't know what this means but little Simon says hurry up and have another baby, I want to come back.'

I burst into tears – no one knew we had given him that name, not even my mother.'

3 Cartoonist, Tony Hart

'A spooky thing happened to Jean's best friend many years ago, when her children were small. The youngest always kicked his bedclothes off at night. When his parents went to bed they'd always go in and straighten them. One night, they found the covers had been beautifully arranged and all his toys had been put at the bottom of the bed.

This happened again, many times. The poltergeist – or whoever he was – had a sense of humour too, he kept pulling the lavatory chain.'

4 Actress, Lindsay Wagner

'In 1979, my mother and I were booked to leave Chicago on an American Airlines DC10. Just before boarding I got this terrible feeling – I knew we shouldn't get on. So we cancelled. Seconds after it had taken off, the plane crashed and everyone on board was killed. Now I trust my psychic feelings and have used them to guide my career as well as my personal life.'

e) Lindsay and her mother cancelled the American Airlines flight after _____
_____

GRAMMAR

Past Perfect or Past Simple?

4   Change the verbs in brackets to either the Past Perfect or the Past Simple. If they can take either, write down both forms.

a) Until I (*explain*) the situation to her I felt guilty.
   Until I __had explained__ / __explained__ the situation to her I felt guilty.

b) After I (*finish*) my lunch I went back to work.

   _____

   _____

c) When the police (*interview*) me they let me go home.

   _____

   _____

d) As soon as I got home my brother (*go out*).

   _____

   _____

e) The children had to stay in until the rain (*stop*).

   _____

   _____

f) When I (*see*) John coming towards me I walked in the other direction.

   _____

   _____

g) I phoned my mother to find out why she (*not write*) for so long.

   _____

Past Perfect Simple or Continuous?

5   Use the cues in brackets to continue the sentences using the Past Perfect Simple or the Past Perfect Continuous.

a) My landlord threw me out of my flat because (*not pay the rent for six months / and break all the windows*).

   My landlord threw me out of my flat because I hadn't paid the rent for six months, and I'd broken all the windows.

b) When I eventually got to the meeting I was bad tempered and exhausted! I (*sit in traffic jam 45 minutes / motorist bump into me / and get completely lost*).

   _____

   _____

   _____

c) By the time 5 o'clock arrived Brenda was furious. She (*wait for an hour / drink six cups of tea / and they still not arrived*).

   _____

   _____

   _____

   _____

d) I was depressed that I couldn't do the exam. I (*study every day for two months / and give up seeing my friends*).

   _____

   _____

   _____

Sequencing events

6 Use these notes to write a ghost story. Use the Past Perfect Simple and Continuous where necessary and add anything else, (prepositions, articles, etc.) that might be necessary.

a) Jill and Nick / on holiday / Scotland / parents and cousin, Steve.
Jill and Nick were on holiday in Scotland with
their parents and cousin, Steve.

b) They / read in newspaper / house next door / haunted.

_____

_____

_____

c) One night / after parents go to bed / Jill and Nick / go out.

_____

_____

_____

d) They ask Steve to come / but / he say / too scared.

_____

_____

_____

e) Shortly after / they arrive / hear / strange noise / see white shape in garden.

_____

_____

_____

f) They scream / run away.

_____

_____

g) Then / hear laughing / see / that someone chase them / down street.

_____

_____

_____

h) It was cousin / who / dressed up in white sheet / to frighten them.

_____

_____

_____

VOCABULARY

Ways of speaking

7 Fill in the gaps with one of the following words in the correct form. Some words are used as verbs and some as nouns.

| whisper gossip groan chat scream swear |

a) He ___screamed___ in terror as the lion came towards him.

b) I've just been _____ to Sue about her new car.

c) Please don't _____ in front of the customers. It doesn't give a good impression.

d) They were talking in a _____ so that nobody could hear them.

e) Don't believe all the _____ you hear about his love affairs.

f) There were loud _____ when he told them the bad news.

Say, speak, tell or *talk*?

8 Fill in the gaps below with the appropriate form of *say, speak, tell* or *talk*.

a) He always _____*tells*_____ his son a story at night.

b) He never stops _____.

c) Could you _____ up, please? I'm a bit deaf.

d) That's exactly what I was just _____ to Olga.

e) Have you got anything to _____ before we finish?

f) Do you _____ English?

g) Could you _____ me the time, please?

Make or *do*?

9 Put the words in the box into the appropriate column, according to whether they go with *make* or *do*.

| your homework   an exam |
| an appointment   the dishes |
| business   a journey   progress |
| harm   a mistake   a complaint |

make

_____

_____

_____

_____

_____

do

___*your homework*___

_____

_____

_____

_____

PRONUNCIATION

Diphthongs

10 One word in each of the following groups has a different diphthong sound from the other words. Underline the odd word out. Then at the head of each column write the pronunciation symbol which corresponds to the diphthong sound in the other three words. Use the pronunciation chart in the Students' Book to help you.

A	B	C	D
/eə/	_____	_____	_____
where	die	crowd	ghost
pair	buy	though	moan
<u>cheer</u>	shine	proud	post
tear (*verb*)	eight	now	mouse

So strong

LISTENING

1 [📟 19.1]   Listen to Nancy's story and circle *Yes* or *No* for the following statements.

a) One summer Nancy worked for a local company. (*Yes/No*)
b) Customers always had to pay for their goods in advance. (*Yes/No*)
c) Nancy worked on the telephones. (*Yes/No*)
d) All the other people in her office were over 65. (*Yes/No*)
e) They all ignored the new female employee. (*Yes/No*)
f) The bosses were all men. (*Yes/No*)
g) Most of the workers were men. (*Yes/No*)
h) The new male employee had to bring up children. (*Yes/No*)
i) He was paid more than the women. (*Yes/No*)

2   Answer these questions.

a) Why do American college students usually work in the holidays?
_____

b) What was Nancy's job in the company?
_____

c) How could the company have its own credit card?
_____

d) Why did the older woman have to work?
_____

e) What did Nancy think was unfair?
_____

f) What reason did the company give for their decision?
_____

3   Listen again and fill in the gaps.

a) When I _____ every summer.
b) A credit clerk is someone who _____ their credit card bills.
c) And we were all college students: _____ for the summer.
d) ... about 65. And she'd _____
   had lost his job, which _____ forty years ...
e) ... difficult at the beginning because _____
   the last thirty or forty years ...
f) Shortly after that _____ job.
g) ... bosses, a man, and said, 'Why _____
   And of course ...
h) ... nothing we could do. They _____
   supporting a family.

GRAMMAR

The passive

4 Complete each sentence using a passive construction.

a) 'I'm glad that horrible man _has been caught._'
(*catch* – Present Perfect Simple).
'Yes, I'm sure he _____
to prison.' (*send* – *will*-future)

b) 'When I saw him he _____
_____ by the police.'
(*question* – Past Continuous)
'I think he _____
a very long sentence.' (*give* – *should*)

c) 'The postman told me he _____
_____ by a dog.' (*bite* – Past Perfect Simple)
'_____ to hospital?'
(*take (he)* – Past Simple)

d) 'I hear that a lot of Irish jokes _____
_____ in tonight's show.'
(*included* – Present Perfect Simple)
'Oh no! I hate it when insulting jokes _____
_____ about other
nationalities.' (*tell* – Present Simple)

5 Put the verbs in the correct form of the passive.

a) The date of Buddha's birth (*now, think*) _____
_____ to be 563 BC.

b) I'm sure if you left a note, you (*not, disturb*)
_____.

c) So far this year thousands of pounds (*raise*)
_____
for famine relief.

d) I doubt if your President (*elect*) _____
_____ for another term of office.
He's too old.

e) I feel sorry for you. Nobody likes (*give*) _____
_____ the sack.

f) R.K. Narayan's third novel (*first, publish*) _____
_____ in 1945.

g) When I got home, I found my car (*steal*) _____
_____.

h) Do you remember I called to see you once
while your office (*repaint*) _____
_____?

VOCABULARY

Words often confused

6 Match the first half of each sentence on the left with its second half on the right.

a) *lose, fail, miss*
She doesn't know where she lost   the class.
Diane failed   her keys.
Ann arrived too late and missed   her music exams.

b) *beat, win, earn*
She beat   at cards.
He never wins   as a teacher.
You don't earn much   him at tennis.

c) *spill, drop, fall*
He spilt   over in the mud.
Raymond dropped   wine on his trousers.
The soldier fell   the box on his foot.

7 Complete the sentences using the words in *italics* in the correct form.

a) *be born, birthday*

i) Shakespeare _____ in 1564.

ii) Where were you on your _____?

b) *rise, raise*

i) I see they've _____ their prices yet again.

ii) Prices _____ sharply last month.

c) *remark, notice*

i) 'I don't much like him,' he _____.

ii) Did you _____ anything odd?

d) *confuse, embarrass*

i) He _____ us with his complicated directions.

ii) I was _____ when Mike starting telling me about his marriage.

e) *advise, announce*

i) The Government's plans have now been _____ to the public.

ii) The doctor _____ Anita to rest.

PRONUNCIATION

Contrastive stress

8 Complete the sentences and circle the word that would probably be stressed.

a) 'I prefer brown bread, don't you?'

'No, I *prefer (white) bread.*' _____

b) 'I thought you lived in Japan.'

'Well, you're wrong. I _____

_____,'

c) 'There are more women students at this university than men students.'

'Really! I thought _____

_____,'

d) 'Have the three parcels arrived?'

'Well, one has arrived but _____

_____,'

e) 'Last week the weather wasn't too bad but _____

_____,'

f) 'You drive an old, green sports car, don't you?'

'No, it's _____,'

Silent letters

9 In many English words, one or more letters may not actually be pronounced (e.g. g*h*ost, dou*b*t). Use your dictionary to help you in the following exercises.

a) Circle the words in the box in which the letter *h* is not pronounced. Underline the words in which *b* is not pronounced.

> lamb hurt honest able behind doubt
> absent hour climbing whole exhausted

b) Cross out the unpronounced consonant letters in each of the words in the box.

> wrong know iron listen talk daughter

c) Complete the spellings.

cu__board   si__n   recei__t   cha__k

autum__   plou__ __   ya__ __t

WRITING

Similar spellings

10 Circle the correct alternative in each sentence, using your dictionary to help you.

a) Have you written anything in your *dairy/diary* today?

b) The present situation threatens world *peace/piece*.

c) This necklace has been *prized/priced* at over £500.

d) Should we *greet/great* him with a kiss?

e) This cake has a lot of *reasons/raisins* in it.

f) Can I *pour/poor* you another cup of tea?

11 With the help of a dictionary choose from the letters in brackets to complete the gaps, using one or two letters for each gap.

a) Please ____*nsure* you are there on time! (*i, e*)

b) This Government has reduced the unions to a state of *imp____t____nce*. (*a, e, r, o*)

c) His eyes were *m____st* with tears. (*i, o*)

d) I can't stand people who tell *l____s*! (*y, e, i, a*)

e) Pat and Ted *sui____* each other very well. (*e, t*)

f) I suppose you'll *c____rse* me for ruining your life. (*u, o*)

Revision

GRAMMAR

Review of verb forms

1 Circle the correct form of the verbs in brackets in the text opposite.

Sentence transformation

2 In each of the following items complete the second sentence so that it has a similar meaning to the first one. In some cases you will have to change the verb.

a) 'We must leave before six,' she said to us.
She told *us we had to leave before six.*

b) She first moved into that house in 1989.
She has _____
_____

c) He lives next door and he's really unpleasant.
The man _____
_____

d) It's not necessary to knock.
You _____
_____

e) It is possible that those people not having an injection will get cholera.
If you _____
_____

f) There is no coffee left.
There isn't _____

g) Someone has told her the news.
She _____

h) Unfortunately, I don't live in a hot country.
She wishes _____
_____

i) We have made very little progress.
Not _____
_____

j) I can't buy your car because I haven't got enough money.
If I _____
_____

A Businessman's Dream!

One day, when businessman Terry Davies and his family (1 *flew / were flying*) back to Britain after a holiday in Tenerife he (2 *had announced / announced*): 'I have made a decision! I (3 *will / am going to*) give up the business – I've had enough!'

His family (4 *were / have been*) surprised but very pleased. A few months later after they (5 *had sold / used to sell*) their house, they (6 *were moving / moved*) to a remote farmhouse without any electricity.

Terry and his family (7 *had been living / lived*) in luxury up to that time, owning a country cottage, a Porsche, and several racehorses. However, for quite a long time they (8 *were feeling / had been feeling*) depressed with this kind of lifestyle.

Terry's wife Katrina remembers their life then. 'I (9 *used to spend / have spent*) all weekend preparing dinners for business people. All they (10 *talked / were talking*) about was what they (11 *bought / had bought*) and how much it (12 *was costing / had cost*). We (13 *used to feel / were feeling*) more and more depressed all the time.'

To the astonishment of their friends they (14 *escaped / were escaping*) to Wales, where they (15 *lived / have been living*) for the past eight months. They (16 *work / worked*) a fourteen hour day, looking after animals and leading a simple country life.

'We (17 *have learned / had learned*) that it is important to do what you want,' said Katrina. 'We (18 *don't know / aren't knowing*) what (19 *will happen / is happening*) when the children (20 *go / will go*) to school, but for the near future our home is here.'

(from *Bella*)

Spot the errors

3 There is a grammatical error in each of the following sentences. Underline the error and then correct it.

a) I would like <u>going</u> on holiday but I can't afford it.

I would like **to go** on holiday but I can't afford it.

b) I am used to speak French but now I can't.

c) I will wait until they will arrive.

d) He is scared at tarantulas.

e) I haven't got some milk.

f) You don't eat meat, don't you?

g) I came here for to find a job.

h) She speaks very fastly.

i) How long time has he been working here?

j) I'll ring up you later.

k) I wasn't listening him when he told me.

PRONUNCIATION

Sounds

4 In each of the following sets circle one word which contains a different vowel or diphthong sound from the other three words. Use your dictionaries if you like.

a) co**u**ple, bl**oo**d, m**u**st, (c**ou**gh)

b) s**i**t, b**ui**ld, t**ea**, Engl**i**sh

c) f**oo**d, p**u**t, s**ou**p, j**ui**ce

d) w**ea**r, p**ai**r, ch**ee**r, t**ea**r (_verb_)

e) l**o**st, w**a**tch, m**o**st, wr**o**ng

f) d**ie**, **ei**ght, b**uy**, sh**i**ne

g) h**o**rse, s**aw**, b**ou**ght, w**o**rd

h) fr**ie**nd, b**ea**n, h**ea**lth, s**ay**s

i) h**ea**rt, **au**nt, h**a**rd, l**a**nd

VOCABULARY

Word building

5 Change the words in brackets so that they can go in the gaps. If necessary, add a prefix.

a) I was very _____interested_____ in what she was saying. (_interest_)

b) We were amazed at how _____ the countryside looks. (_beauty_)

c) The police are not always successful at catching _____. (_crime_)

d) It was an extremely _____ meeting after all. (_use_)

e) She _____ and missed the bus. (_sleep_)

f) I'll have to _____ my composition – it's a bit untidy. (_write_)

g) The government won great _____ with their reforms. (_popular_)

h) Although they liked the house they had to _____ the kitchen. (_modern_)

i) I love my car but it's very _____ in bad weather. (_rely_)

j) A lot of people in the world are dying of _____. (_hungry_)

Test your vocabulary

6 All the vocabulary in this section has appeared in the Workbook.

a) The person you call when you have problems with the water pipes. ____plumber____

b) Your brother's wife. _____

c) The Americans call it a _pharmacy_. _____

d) When you phone someone you have to _____ the number.

e) This word means both _good_ (e.g. _good_ weather) and _the money you have to pay when you have committed an offence._ _____

f) A house on one level, with no upstairs. _____

g) The opposite of _fresh_ bread. _____

h) If you are similar in looks and/or personality to your parents you _____ them.

i) A fly is an _____.

j) A phrasal verb for _cancel_ is _____.

WRITING

Linking expressions

7 Use the words in brackets to link the sentences below in two different ways, making sure you pay attention to the punctuation. In each case one of the linking expressions can connect the two sentences to make one sentence.

a) Dogs are noisy. They eat a lot. (*and / as well*)

Dogs are noisy and they eat a lot.

Dogs are noisy. They eat a lot as well.

b) I finished my meal. I went out. (*then/after*)

_____

_____

_____

_____

c) She was watching television. He was cooking the meal. (*while/meanwhile*)

_____

_____

_____

_____

d) He had a bath. He phoned her. (*afterwards/ before*)

_____

_____

_____

_____

e) Everyone else enjoyed the film. I found it very boring. (*although/however*)

_____

_____

_____

f) I didn't study at all. I failed my exams. (*so / as a result*)

_____

_____

_____

g) I wasn't hungry. I ate the meal. (*even though / nevertheless*)

_____

_____

_____

_____

Dictation

8 [📼 20.1] Listen to the recording as many times as you want, and complete the gaps in the text. Check your punctuation.

A: I once _____

_____

who needed a skeleton for his studies. _____

_____,

so he decided to go to a cemetery …

B: _____

A: Yes, _____,

old coffin he could hear groaning, _____

_____

_____ grabbed the first thing he could see,

_____.

B: What happened next?

A: Well, _____

_____. He rushed up the stairs,

_____ where he lived,

_____.

B: I suppose _____

A: No. _____

_____. Then he heard

_____. Someone

_____.

The noise stopped at his door, _____

_____,

the handle starting to turn, and he heard this voice saying, _____.

B: And did he?

A: Oh yes. _____

_____ at whatever it was.

And that's the end of the story!

Tapescripts

Unit 4

RECORDING 1

SARAH: I didn't know any Italian at all before I came to Italy, and so it was like being thrown in the middle of a different world, really. But, what I found was it was very, very difficult at the beginning, all – I tried to read the newspapers, I went to the cinema, I had lots of Italian friends and I, a lot of the time I was a bit lost, to tell the truth at the beginning, and I didn't really speak a lot. But then suddenly, after about a month, I started recognising things that they said, and I started recognising things that I'd read, and suddenly I could be much braver and try things out and, well I know I made loads of mistakes but people didn't really seem to mind – they helped me. And I carried on doing all the things that I did before and everything became easier. I think now, I mean I've got to the stage where communicating is no problem at all. I mean, I can say mostly what I want and I can understand people, but I, I do make a lot of mistakes and I think it is going to be very, very difficult to get past this stage. I'm really pretty inaccurate grammatically.

PAM: It was a, a small class, with a very nice teacher, so the atmosphere was great, very relaxed, and I think that helped me a lot. But the way we learned was very traditional in the sense that we learnt, we were given lists of vocabulary to learn. We had quite a lot of reading and then answering questions or, very little of the class was in German. And then I went on to study German at university and there it was all translation work, no conversation at all. And then, in my third year I went over and studied a year in Germany, and I found it was quite a shock because there I was, I'd studied two years at university and four years at school, and I was, on paper, very good, but I couldn't really communicate with people. I think what really helped was that once I'd found myself some friends over there I then started to relax. I mean in two, three months I learned more than I'd learned in the previous five years, about actually using the language to communicate.

Unit 6

RECORDING 1

1 Last night my dad sent his car in to change to unleaded petrol and I think it helps because the, the fumes aren't as powerful and all the fumes are helping to, to destroy the ozone layer.

2 It's not only people that are worse off for the fumes it's the animals as well because, say, tankers carrying oil, if they spill, then all the animals get, become covered in tar and they can't survive and all the beaches are being ruined.

3 Well, I think that, about the countryside there are definitely not enough people aware of what's going on. There are lots of pesticides and things sprayed over the plants, and then people eat them and the chemical pollution in this country we've said is higher than in other countries. In the sea other countries are very careful, and yet our pollution is just spreading all over the world. We're just not trying. I mean, in, our parents, they're trying to clean the house and everything, but they're not aware what of they're using!

4 I think some more young people should set up clubs and things instead of just sitting in front of computers and things, instead of actually doing something about their environment because it's going to affect them when they grow up.

5 I think when we grow up the world might be a better place in the sense of technology and things, but so, what's so important about technology if we have no grass, no animals, no trees, no nothing except computers, and that, they've got no feeling in them?

Unit 8

RECORDING 1

INTERVIEWER: Kevin, could you tell me whether people in Britain prefer to rent houses or buy them?

KEVIN MOLL: On the whole they prefer to buy houses, for several reasons. It is now, after many years really a British way of life. People, now, it's now bred into them that they should buy their house rather than rent their house. It's, it's thought of, renting, that it's a waste of money. You're throwing money away. And also, buying a property is seen as a very, very sound investment for your future.

I: And what sort of houses do single people tend to go for?

K: By single people you're usually refering to younger people, and money is the major constraint, is how much you can afford. So it tends to be smaller properties such as flats, one-, two-bedroom apartments, studio apartments, that sort of thing.

I: And young couples?

K: Young couples then tend to, both of them tend to be in jobs so therefore their earning capabilities, their earning power's greater. They can afford slightly bigger properties such as a two-bedroom apartment, then on to small cottages, and small houses.

I: And what about old people?

K: Older people tend to be scaling down their activities, buying smaller houses, and therefore it tends to be bungalows, which are easy to run and easy for them to run around in.

I: So on the whole do old houses or new houses tend to be more expensive?

K: The older properties on the whole tend to be more expensive. The likeness is to an oil painting. Because of the rarity of these old properties there are, there are far more modern houses than older properties, they tend to be more expensive. Also the character of them. They tend to be more picturesque. Internally they've got old beams, big fireplaces, and appeal to a lot of people, but there are not that many of them, so they tend to be more expensive.

I: And when people are looking for houses, what specific things do they tend to look for?

K: One of the major problems when looking for a house is what somebody can afford. They may want a big mansion with lots of land, swimming pool, etc., but can't actually afford it. However they may have two children and they will therefore need three bedrooms. If it's a question of having young children for example, they will need a garden of some sort for them to play in. When the children are much older and have passed their driving test and have got cars themselves they will therefore need more parking and a garage to take care of the increase in number of cars. If somebody has, for example, a major hobby as a gardener, they will require a garden shed so they can put all their tools in.

I: And finally Kevin, if you could choose any house at all to live in which would you choose?

K: It would certainly have to have its long, sweeping, private drive. Preferably with river frontage and its own mooring for a massive yacht, but also require a jacuzzi, sauna, squash court, tennis court, indoor swimming pool and possibly a small flat attached to it.

I: So in fact the house isn't very important at all.

K: Not at all.

I: Thanks very much, Kevin.

K: Yeh, pleasure.

Unit 10

RECORDING 1

KEITH: In, in twenty years time there'll be very, very few young people and there'll be many older people, and, for example, in Britain at the moment there's no compulsory military service. I can see some form of compulsory military service coming back into being, being reintroduced. I think we're not going to be able to have private motorcars in twenty years time: that's just not going to be on. People are becoming increasingly critical or unwilling to have motorways in their back gardens and even railway lines in their back gardens and somehow we're just going to have to get used to being less mobile or being mobile in a different kind of way.

JENNY: So if I think about ten or twenty years time, I, I imagine that if things go well then what I see is a world where green issues have become quite powerful. So we might have, we might have people who care more about what's happening to the planet, we might have supermarkets full of what – what are they called? – ecologically friendly products. We might have more care and concern about parts of the world where there are now droughts and things like that, and then on the other hand, the sort of the bad side, is that things will be exactly as they are now, if not worse. The environment will have been impoverished more, there'll be fewer forests, there'll be people still not caring about what happens to the land and the people on the marginal areas of land. So I don't, yes, I suppose – it's, it's a question of 'goodies' and 'baddies' really – if the 'goodies' get, become more powerful then there will be a better world.

Unit 11

RECORDING 1

a)

OPTICIAN: Can you read the bottom line?
PATIENT: Sorry.
OPTICIAN: What about the line above?
PATIENT: Er, no.
OPTICIAN: How many letters can you see?
PATIENT: None at all, I'm afraid.
OPTICIAN: Well, we'd better get you some new lenses then, hadn't we?

b)

HAIRDRESSER: Have a look at these colours.
CUSTOMER: This one's a bit too light I think. I, I don't want it to look too obviously dyed.
HAIRDRESSER: What about this one?
CUSTOMER: Oh, that looks all right. Would it look OK, do you think?
HAIRDRESSER: I think so.
CUSTOMER: Let's try it then. We can always wash it out.

c)

MIDWIFE: How often have you been having them?
MOTHER: Every three minutes.
MIDWIFE: Where's your husband?
MOTHER: He's gone to get me some sweets.
MIDWIFE: No, you mustn't have those now. Come on, now. Try to relax and remember your breathing.

d)

TRAVEL AGENT: No, there's no flight available.
CUSTOMER: I'm sorry, I thought I would be able to get a week off work but I just can't.
TRAVEL AGENT: I might be able to find something in this country.
CUSTOMER: No, I don't think so. Can I get my money back?
TRAVEL AGENT: Sorry, it's non-refundable.

e)

PLUMBER: Is there a direct supply?
CUSTOMER: Yes, if you put it next to the sink.
PLUMBER: I'll need to put a tap on the pipes.
CUSTOMER: OK. When can you connect it up?
PLUMBER: What about tomorrow morning?
CUSTOMER: That's fine.

Unit 13

RECORDING 1

BONNIE: I've had a recurring dream since I was a child and it's about flying. But the strange thing is I don't actually get very high. I only fly as far as the treetops and I have to run and then get off the ground, but there are people chasing me. They never catch me and sometimes the dream is, is nice, pleasant, because I, I feel as if I've got away from these people quite easily and I'm flying and it's, it's, it's nice, it's not menacing at all. But other times it is quite menacing because, though I get away from the people or whoever it is chasing me, it seems to take a longer time, and it, it just feels menacing. And I think, I think it means that, it's, it's obviously some sort of insecurity, and it's means I'm in a situation perhaps that I want to get out of.

BEN: A recurring nightmare that I have, and I know I have this in common with other teachers because I've talked to them about it, is that I walk into a classroom, I'm standing there, and it suddenly occurred to me not only that I've not prepared anything for it but that I haven't the faintest idea what I'm doing there, what the lesson is all about, who the students are or what I'm supposed to be teaching. If it's in one of the extreme forms, I'm also naked, which I take to be sort of symbolic of the, of, of the same thing. And I think this kind of horror of unpreparedness is a, is a thing that all teachers have and that must be what the dream is, is all about.

KEITH: My mother died about two years ago, and for about a month after her death I had incredibly vivid dreams about meeting her, very often in strange places. I can remember one where, where I met her amongst some rocks in what was a desert-like place, and she was the way she had been before her illness. She was very ill for about a year before her death. And she, so she was very sort of lively and sprightly, and I remember in every dream I'd say, 'But what are you doing here? You shouldn't be here. You're dead.' And it was very much a fact. I don't remember her answer. It wasn't saying, 'No, I'm not dead at all' or 'No, you dreamt that', but it was, 'This is absolutely normal: there's nothing unusual or odd about this.' I think they were nice dreams. There was never any sense of nightmare about them. They were just odd. It was this surprise each time of being in a dream and, and, and, meeting Mum, and she was very, very much alive.

Unit 15

RECORDING 1

ED: Well, my wife's Chinese, so we eat quite a lot of Chinese food, usually at home. Other sorts of food? I quite like Italian food, so I occasionally try and cook some spaghetti and things like that. I love Indian food, but I'm not very good at cooking it, so usually if we, we eat Indian food we go out to a restaurant.

As to the type of food I eat, I don't eat a lot of meat. I do eat things like chicken and turkey – white meats – but I don't eat a lot of pork and beef, usually because, well beef especially is not supposed to be very good for you so I try to cut down on that. Fish, I love, but I don't eat a lot of because it's rather expensive to get good fresh fish anyway. Vegetables, I like a lot of, broccoli especially – that's one of my favourite ones – courgettes, peas, things like that, so usually have a good balance of vegetables with the, with the meal. In summer I eat quite a lot of salads when it's, especially when it's very hot, but in the winter I usually find it's, it's a bit cold for salads. And usually have some fruit, try to have some fruit each day. Apples, I love cox's apples, they're very nice. Usually have an orange each day and I also love bananas.

Drinks? I usually drink tea, but not Indian tea much any more, usually herbal teas. I used to drink gallons and gallons of Indian tea but I found a few years ago that it was keeping me awake at night because of all the caffeine, so I started drinking things like camomile and peppermint tea instead. I rarely ever drink soft drinks because they've got a lot of sugar. I try to avoid those things. I find the sugar's bad for my skin. Same with food: I try to eat food without sugar. Alcohol I usually only drink at weekends. I go out to the pub, maybe on a Friday or Saturday night, and have a few pints of beer. I don't usually drink spirits like whisky or, or wi-, or wine and things like that.

I've never really been on a diet to lose weight, but I did go on a diet a few years ago to try and increase my weight because I found that I was getting a bit skinny. I'm only about eleven stone and I find that if I don't eat three good meals a day I lose weight very quickly, so I have to be very careful and make sure I, I eat a lot.

When I go shopping I like to look at the ingredients' list on packaged food because I try to avoid some of the modern additives that you get in food, especially when I see a long list of E numbers I usually think that's probably not too good for me and I avoid that. And things like monosodium glutamate that you can get in some foods I try and avoid that. Otherwise I eat most sort of foods.

Unit 17

RECORDING 1

BRUCE: Actually I'm terrified of deep water. I think it may be because I fell into a pond when I was two years old and I nearly drowned. But now, whenever, I don't like going out of my depth, and I'm actually terrified of looking down into the water and seeing all those dark objects down there. I really don't like it at all.

SUE: The only thing that I really have a phobia about is wasps. And I know that I should keep still if there's a wasp in the room, and I know I shouldn't move, and I know it won't hurt me if I don't move, but my reason tells me all this, but I just can't stay still if there is a wasp in the room. I just have to move away or run away if it gets too close. So I certainly have a phobia about wasps, not bees but wasps. I just can't bear them. Wasps look aggressive to me and they seem to behave aggressively, and I, I believe that they're out to get me, whereas bees are much gentler things and, and sort of they're going, they're going about their business, as it were.

JANE: I'm quite claustrophobic. I don't like lifts. I don't like going underground. I got talked into going into the caves in Derbyshire once, much against my better judgement. I managed to fall flat on my face in the mud and not be allowed out until the tour was finished, so I had to walk around dripping in mud. I don't think I'll ever go in a cave again. I don't like going below decks in ships or anything like that. I'd much rather be up high and looking out on to things.

MARIE: I think the fear of falling into a hole is, is a real fear, simply because of something I experienced as a child when I was dancing on the, on a well that had been covered by a piece of metal, and I hadn't realised that there was a, there was a great hole underneath what I was dancing on. And when I did, in fact, look over the side and saw, and saw a, a, what seemed like, just an endless pit of darkness, I think that created a tremendous fear of heights.

Unit 19

RECORDING 1

NANCY: When I was at college, I worked every summer. This is because American college students have to work usually to pay the tuition fees. And they work in the summers and in the holidays and sometimes even during the semesters.

Anyway, this one summer I was working in a local company near my home, and I worked as a credit clerk. A credit clerk is someone who calls people up and asks them to please pay their credit card bills. That's because this company was a very large company and it had its own credit card.

Anyway, that summer as I was working in the credit office of this company there were three of us. And we were all college students: we were only going to be there for the summer. It was a short term job. And they, one of them left, and so they hired someone else, an older woman, about 65. And she'd had to go back to work because her husband had lost his job, which he had worked at for forty years but he'd been made redundant anyway. And he couldn't find another job, so she had to try and find one. She found it pretty difficult at the beginning because she had been a housewife working at home for the last thirty or forty years, but we all liked her a lot and we all tried to help her in absolutely every way we could, and she was coming along nicely. And it was really important to her 'cause she was supporting a family.

Shortly after that they hired a middle-aged man to do the same job. And after about a week or so we found out somehow that they were paying him 25% more than they were paying all the rest of us. He didn't have any more qualifications than we did. He didn't have any more experience. But he was getting 25% more. So we went to the, one of the bosses, and of course in this company 95% of the workforce were women, but all of the bosses were men. So we went up to one of the bosses, a man, and said 'Why is this man getting paid more: 25% more?' And of course the answer was, 'Because he's a man.' 'Why should a man get paid 25% more than us?' we said. 'He hasn't got any more experience. He hasn't got any more qualifications.' 'Well, because he's got a family,' said the boss. This we knew the answer to. 'No he hasn't,' we said. 'He lives with his mother, and his mother pays the bills.' 'Ah,' said our boss. 'Well, he …' and he thought carefully. 'He might have a family some day.'

And that was that: end of the conversation. There was nothing we could do. They wouldn't give us any more, not even the woman who was supporting a family. But it was just for the man who might some day have a family. And I thought that was pretty unfair.

Pearson Education Limited
Edinburgh Gate
Harlow
Essex
CM20 2JE
England
and Associated Companies throughout the world.
www.longman-elt.com

First published 1991
Twelfth impression 2000

Set in Linotronic 300 ITC Garamond Light 10/12pt

Printed in Italy
by G. Canale & C. S.p.A. - Borgaro T.se - Turin

ISBN 0 582 04665 3

Acknowledgements

Illustrated by
Julie Anderson, David Brindley, Joan Corlass,
Lorraine Harrison, Pauline Hazelwood and Wendy Sinclair.

We are grateful to the following for permission to
reproduce photographs and other copyright material;
Animal Aid, page 56 below right; Ardea London, page 56
above (photo Bryan L. Sage); Barnaby's Picture Library,
pages 27 centre right (photo Ad Lib), 28 (e), 58 bear
(photo Michael J. Corley) and gorilla (photo Mustograph);
Bella, page 42; John Birdsall Photography, page 27 far
right; Camera Press, pages 10 (photo TASS), 17 below
(photo CAF Warsaw) and 38 below centre (photo Vernon
Merriot); J. Allan Cash Photolibrary, pages 8, 27 far left and
centre left, 28 (c) and 58 zebra; Bruce Coleman, pages 57
(photo Leonard Lee Rue III), 58 giraffe (photo Mark N.
Boulton), tiger (photo Jane Burton), kangaroo (photo Hans
Reinhard), hippo (photo Peter Davey) and leopard (photo
Masood Qureshi); Format Photographers, page 38 below
left (photo Brenda Prince); Will Green, page 49; Sally and
Richard Greenhill, page 28 (a) and (b); Kobal Collection,
page 60; Mills and Boon 1988, Robyn Donald, *Mansion for
My Love*, page 24; Network Photographers, page 38 above
right (photo Mike Abrahams); Photo Co-op, pages 28 (d,
photo Gina Glover) and 38 centre right (photo Janis
Austin); Solo Syndication, page 4 (photo *Woman's Realm/*
IPC Magazines); Tony Stone Worldwide, page 38 below
right (photo Julian Calder); Syndication International, page
17 above; Telegraph Colour Library, page 70 (photo
International Stock Photography); The Vegetarian Society,
page 56 below left.

The photograph on page 7 was taken by John Birdsall;
pages 14 and 53 by Longman Photographic Unit; page 67
by Nigel Luckhurst, Cambridge.

We are grateful to the following for permission to
reproduce copyright material;

the author's agent for an adaptation of the article
'Tarantula: crawly, but not creepy' by David Alderton from
Best magazine 30.4.88; Associated Press Ltd for an
adaptation of the article 'Quake ordeal of mother and
child' from *The Times* January 1989; H Bauer Publishing
Ltd for an adaptation of the article 'It costs a pretty packet!'
by Con Smith from *Bella* magazine 30.7.88 and an adapted
extract from the article 'A Businessman's Dream!' from
Bella magazine 23.7.88; Hamfield Publications Ltd for an
adaptation of the article "Wouldn't it be lovely to get a
good night's sleep!' by Dr Johnson from *Plus* magazine,
Issue No 6; IPC Magazines Ltd for an adaptation of an
article about Jenny Agutter by Debra Hamblin from
Woman's Realm 18.10.88 and an adapted extract from the
article 'Dental Terror' from *Chat* magazine 13.8.88.

We have been unable to trace the copyright holders in the
articles about Tony Hart, Carol Hawkins, Lindsay Wagner
and Barbara Woodhouse and would appreciate any
information that would enable us to do so.